This book reflects the author's present recollections of experiences over time. Some names and characteristics have been changed, some events have been compressed, and some dialogue has been recreated.

Dedication

I want to thank my daughter, Tiffany Webster. You are my accountability partner, who keeps me focused. You motivated me every day to complete this book. I also want to thank my daughter Taylor for reading my manuscript and giving me a Generation Z viewpoint. Christian, Tiffany, and Taylor: you make me proud. Your kindness, empathy, and selfless spirits have benefitted others.

Thank you to my wife and high school sweetheart, Deborah. I have learned a lot from our journey from meager beginnings and childhood adversity –that hidden trauma of the past can disrupt a marriage, but unconditional love and forgiveness conquers all. I am proud how far we have grown together and have raised empathetic children.

Thank you to my deceased grandparents James, and Ellen Webster, who raised and buffered me from the stress of life; you taught me to be compassionate and empathic. You showed me by example why it is always better to give than to receive.

Thank you to my mother, Ellen Wells -- there is no greater love than the love a child has for his mother. I love you. I will always be thankful for your help over the years.

Thank you to my uncle Cliff, you are the quintessential father figure, role model, and mentor. You show me how a good man behaves, treat others, and support his community. You changed the trajectory of my life when you had me play basketball.

Thank you, Sarah Abrams, for taking time out of your busy schedule and life to read, edit, and give feedback on my book. Your kind comments and encouraging words for my story motivated me to stick with it even when I had my self-doubts. I admire you as a person and I'm grateful for the support you have given my family.

Thank you, Katherine Boo, for your friendship and guidance over the

Dedication

years. You have believed and helped me during hard times. I admire your advocacy and uplifting of disenfranchised people in your book, articles, and other writings.

Thank you, Jane Rand, for your friendship, mentoring, and exposure to books and the gift of learning. You fed my innate intellectual curiosity, which lit a fire in me that has only grown stronger over the years to expand my knowledge in the field of stress and human behavior.

Thank you, Kent Amos, you exposed me to many people, places, and events that expanded my view of greater possibilities in life. You were there when I needed you the most. You gave me the book, Think and Grow Rich in high school. The stories captured my attention and introduced me to the success principles.

Thank you, Sheila Hoban, who read over my early draft many years ago. You were encouraging even though my writing had a long way to go for publication. You saw my potential, and that motivated me to stick with it until done.

Thank you, Ellen Carter Woodbridge, for being a wonderful English teacher, tutor, mentor, and friend. Your kindness and support shown to me over the years is much appreciated. You made a positive difference in my life.

Thank you, Dr. Alexandria Rich. Your editing and organization of my material helped me narrow my focus and hone my writing to complete this book.

CONTENTS

PART 2

INTRODUCTION

The Covid-19 virus has stressed us unlike anything in recent history. Though our emotions have been shaken by uncertainty, isolation, helplessness, and grief, we strive for normalcy and good mental health. There is good stress (eustress) and bad (distress). In fact, we need eustress for growth, to develop, and to flourish; it's essential to life. It's the distressful and traumatic experiences that overload our nervous system. Whether a 100-year pandemic, social stressors, or personal problems, physiologically our bodies react in similar ways to perceived or real (pressures) threats to our safety and survival. When we cannot cope anymore, we feel defeated, which causes symptoms the psychiatric profession has labeled mental illness.

In my twenties, I did not manage major (distressful) life events well. I experienced anxiety disorders (generalized anxiety, panic attacks, agoraphobia, and social anxiety), coupled with major depression disorder. It was a disruptive and painful time for me, like the 40 million people every year in the US who experience anxiety disorders.[1] And then there's depression, announced by the World Health Organization (WHO) in 2017 as the leading cause of ill health and disability worldwide. More than 300 million people worldwide are living with depression.[2] I was afraid to leave my house; social interactions terrorized me, and anxiety attacks made me an insomniac. What's your experience with these conditions? Are you anxious most of the time, and feel unwell in an unreal sense? You cannot concentrate. You feel sad, tired,

---

[1] https://adaa.org/Understanding-Anxiety
[2] Jeffrey Rediger, M.D., Cured: The Life Changing Science of Spontaneous Healing, First Edition: February 2020. Flatiron Books, 120 Broadway, New York, NY 10271. page 116

worthless, and have lost interest in things you enjoyed. You feel numb. The symptoms are unbearable; you are depressed. You are pessimistic. What is happening to me? Why am I feeling this way? Am I going crazy? You may have a long history with your condition, or this may be your first bout. Are you worried, wondering, will I feel normal again? Do not panic—no pun intended. These awful symptoms are a reaction of the nervous system protecting you from overwhelming stress. Like an overloaded circuit breaker, the brain shuts down and you must figure out what is overloading it, lessen your stress (allostatic) load to return normal functioning. Once I understood that, I was less confused and afraid, then I knew I was not going crazy, nor are you.

I spent the quarantine thinking how mental health had worsened for people, especially those with preexisting issues. I looked at my childhood and learned the roots of my anxiety were planted there. That discovery made sense of the poor way I have reacted to stressful experiences throughout my life. Have you considered that how you cope with stress started in childhood?

Some wonder, is there really a connection there? If so, what happened during that period that shaped how I handle stress. It is an obvious question and so is the answer. Research in attachment science show how mothers/fathers and other primary caretakers form attachments, nurture, and bond with children (or lack thereof) in the first two to five years of life (subconscious is highly programmable), laying the foundation for emotional, physical, psychological and behavioral health extending into adulthood. 80 percent of brain growth occurs during this sensitive developmental period, and children are impressionable throughout the formative years.

We enter life neurologically wired for different psycho-social stimuli. Aside from our physical characteristics, we come into the world with genetic predispositions, some for anxiety and depression. It's our environments and what happens in them that affects us. During the early childhood years, stressful and/or traumatic events negatively affect the mind and body.

I have learned from my life and social work career that childhood adversity (attachment ruptures, toxic stress and Adverse Childhood Experiences) causes high stress reactivity in adults. In other words, distressing childhood experiences make some people more susceptible and overly reactive to stressful situations, events, and people than others.

I'll explain these terms in more detail later in the book. We do better when we understand what happened to us and learn from it. Through self-discovery and making sense of our childhood adversity (becoming consciously aware), we can change our thinking and behaviors in a constructive way. Our brains are malleable. For example, we can overcome psychological and emotional wounds through a variety of interventions focused on self-care.

My mental health crisis was 25 years ago. Does that mean I haven't failed or endured new traumas or loss, been disappointed, made mistakes, and gotten down on myself since then? Of course, I have. I'm a human being.

I have learned new coping skills to manage hardships better. I changed my mindset. I dealt with stressful situations, people, and places in a rational and realistic way. I became self-aware, assertive and yet; I am still a work in progress. Like me, you want support and empathy and to feel better—not indifference, apathy, and ridicule.

PREFACE

I showed a colleague the initial book cover of a shadowy human figure in silhouette with its head down, standing on a railroad track. She said, "that looks depressing," with disgust. Her perception that mental illness is a sign of weakness or that a person is crazy, and people should stay away from them stops people from seeking help. It is those long-held misconceptions and stereotypes about mental illness that's taboo.

My intention in writing this book is to help people in distress and to destigmatize mental illness. I hope my story motivates people to examine their childhoods closely for answers to understand how they have influenced their adult stress response and coping styles. Obviously, not all childhoods are problematic, but for those who had some challenges, this book is for you. Lastly, I want people with mental health issues to seek help before their condition advance to a crisis level.

Do not fear being judged or ostracized for needing help. Anxiety disorders are the most common mental illness around the world. I read an article online in the *Harper's Bazaar* magazine in which actress and singer Selena Gomez talked candidly about her struggles with anxiety and depression. She was quoted as saying, "I think it's a battle I'm going to have to face for the rest of my life." Her words resonated with me because I used to think like that, and maybe you do too. There are effective therapies that can bring people relief within weeks—yes, there is something positive to look forward to.

Like myself, countless people have gotten their lives back. They have achieved their goals, or at least are actively working toward them. Your story is still being written. I want you to continue your journey, whatever that might be for you. I want you to be less frightened, less fatalistic, and more hopeful; I want you to take control of your life. I remember when the depression in my mind cleared. I felt more like myself each day. It was a liberating feeling. And the same thing can happen for you.

Do not let mental disorders diminish the talents and gifts you have to offer to the world. You might think life has passed you by and that you are incapable of achieving your goals and dreams, but this isn't so. Please do not give up, because they are well within your reach. When I was in the throes of mental illness, I read many stories of people overcoming adversity, which inspired and motivated me to get better. They gave me hope. It is in that vein that I share mine.

This book has three parts

In Part One, I reflect on my early childhood upbringing, family dynamics (attachments), and social stressors in my community that contributed to my anxiety. That knowledge was vital for me to establish a cause and timeline for my ordeal, and it will help you too. The search for answers is not about looking for someone to blame. By tracing your social history, you will find answers to questions you've had for a long time, which can lead to a successful pathway to heal.

In Part Two, I talk about my transition from childhood to adulthood; in general, this is a stressful period for most people as we take on adult responsibilities. I discuss my struggles as an anxiety-stricken child to a doubtful (overachieving) college scholarship earner. In college, I took a stress management course that made me aware of stress impact on people throughout their life. This information would ultimately be the catalyst for my transformation.

After college was a time of adversity and trauma for me. The breakup from my high school sweetheart, deaths of my beloved grandparents, friends, and raising a child during a public health crisis were daunting. I experienced vicarious trauma as a social worker.

Preface

Despite the adversity, I achieved against the odds, with the help of some special people and lessons learned along the way. I share them in this book. I hope they benefit you.

In Part Three, I discuss the Adverse Childhood Experiences Study (ACE's). It's one of the most important public health studies of our generation. It helped me connect the dots and it will help you too. It's findings show there is a direct correlation between childhood adversity and adult physical, social, and mental health problems. Also, I talk about the importance of self-care to improve physical and mental health. For example, mindfulness, exercise, and yoga are proven self-care practices that will help you manage stress, reduce anxiety, and overcome depression.

Yoga is a whole-body exercise. And it's effective to help people heal from trauma. And of course, we all know the benefits of exercise. Then there is mindfulness, proven to reduce stress, lessen anxiety, and lift depression. You must choose a self-care practice that fits your needs.

Exploring medication is also an available for those wanting a pharmaceutical option. There is a broad variety of professional counseling and therapeutic interventions and pastoral counseling available throughout the country. And telehealth has made therapy more accessible than ever right in your own home. The most important thing in your self-care plan is to make your mental, emotional, spiritual, and physical health improvement a priority.

You can control your destiny, not your past.

PART 1

CHAPTER 1

I Thought I Was Going Crazy

"To know the road ahead, ask those coming back."
Chinese proverb

In quarantine, I reflected on my first experience with mental disorders in my twenties. Though I had not been born with a lot, I had worked hard and been, in many ways, blessed: I had turned a talent for basketball into a great education, and eventually a master's degree in Social Work. I had married my high school sweetheart and had a beautiful two-year-old son. In the months before my visit with a psychiatrist, however, I felt worthless and numb, and I sensed everyone and everything around me was meaningless.

An unfamiliar emptiness entered my body. I would pinch my forearm as hard as I could and barely feel it. I did not hear people talk to me when they were right beside me. It was as if my hearing had gone bad. When I played with my son, Christian, I could not smile or act goofy as much as I adored him. When I read him his favorite book, *Bambi*, the words swam out of focus. I strained my eyes to open wider, trying to clear my clouded mind, but it did not help. My memory was poor, and I could not concentrate. When I was young, I had had some symptoms but nothing as intense as this.

I was sad and felt like crying but could not, and at other times I would cry for no reason. I felt helpless. I was wide awake but could not feel or relate to the everyday happenings. I was afraid I had lost my mind; angst was my new normal.

I stayed at my parents' house in Maryland the weekend before my first psychiatrist visit. I lay in bed restlessly, my eyes shut, unable to fall asleep or stop thinking. My thoughts were fatalistic, and I thought I was going to die. To say I was frightened is an understatement. I was nervous and emotionally detached. I would later learn what I was going through was something called dissociation, which can occur during periods of severe stress. It is a natural way our mind and body protect us when challenges are overwhelming. At the time, I just knew I was desperate.

It was April and spring was in full bloom. In the past I had always found solace in nature, and one morning I went out on my mother's porch to feel better. Her lawn lay before me like nature's most welcoming carpet. Fluttering insects abounded. A rainbow of roses, hyacinth, and tulips spread across the yard. Their fragrance filled the air, and I breathed deeply, yet I felt nothing.

I tried another remedy that worked for me in troubled times before: closing my eyes and positioning my face to take the healing rays of the sun. I waited. I hoped. But my spacey mood and body chills were unchanged. Detachment dulled my senses. I was bewildered and depressed. Here on nature's carpet, I felt like an unwelcome guest.

Before this experience, I was not happy every day (none of us are perpetually happy; that is unrealistic), but my baseline personality was friendly. But now, I did not recognize the person I had become; the old me was gone, or so I believed. My mother had been traveling, and my job that day was to pick her up at the airport.

Beforehand, I mustered enough energy to have breakfast at IHOP, but as I waited to be seated, anxiety washed over me. My heart raced and my breaths were shallow. I felt panic. Flooded by fear, I looked to escape. I became more nervous with each passing moment. I said to myself, "What the hell is wrong with me?" Why was something I had done 100 times before so anxiety-provoking? How could this mundane act of standing in line to eat breakfast be so terrifying? I put my head down, afraid to look around at the people in the restaurant. My mind was irrational. As I ate, I thought everyone could see the real me, the person who was losing his mind. I left breakfast baffled, worried, and more anxious.

Even driving to the airport was different—uncomfortable and distressing. I drove over a bridge and became agitated. I avoided looking at other drivers, holding the steering wheel tighter, afraid to lose control. I felt paranoid, and nervous, but thankfully I made it to the airport in one piece. My mother walked out of the terminal without a care in the world. She smiled, and I faked a smile in return.

On the way home, I told her how I felt. She was a veteran mental health nurse with over 25 years of experience working at psychiatric hospitals such as Saint Elizabeth's and the Veterans Administration. If anyone could help me, I thought, she could.

My voice quavered like a scared child, afraid to tell a parent something bad. I explained my problem.

I said, "I don't feel like myself."

"What's wrong?" she replied. Her jovial attitude changed to concern.

I repeated, "I don't feel like myself. I feel like I am not in my body. It is hard to describe. It's unlike anything I've ever experienced before." Her next response startled me.

"You sound like you're going crazy," she said. She had confirmed my fears, or so I thought. Her words scared me. I was vulnerable and in a suggestible state. In retrospect, what neither of us were aware of at the time was that anxiety disorders and depression symptoms (of which there are over 200[3]) can make you feel like you are going crazy, but you are not. You may feel ashamed of telling others about what you are feeling because they may not understand and may say something that scares you or makes you think you are weak or crazy.

Do not be afraid to reach out for help. If my story sounds familiar, then you or someone you know may have an anxiety disorder or depression or both. These disorders can occur simultaneously; in psychiatry, the term is called comorbidity. Of course, I am not diagnosing you—I will leave that up to the mental health professionals. Everybody's situation is unique and there is no one-size-fits-all approach to mental health diagnosis, treatments, and recovery.

---

[3] https://www.calmclinic.com/anxiety-guide/symptoms

CHAPTER 2

The Beginnings of My Anxiety

My Childhood

My mother shared some information with me just before the publication of this book that she had never told me. I was surprised. It helped me to identify the beginning of my anxiety before I was born. She is a wonderful mother and a kind person. I love her dearly. When she was pregnant with me, she experienced never-ending stress. It was the 1960s; she was 21-years-old, a single mother, expecting her second child in three years while living in a poor neighborhood.

She was afraid and worried about the responsibility of having another baby. My aunt Janiece confirmed that family value to me. She said, "to have a baby without being married in our household was frowned upon." Obviously, my grandparents had deep moral beliefs about bearing children and being accountable. She could not escape or fight those social constructs at the time.

My grandparents were poor and having children was expensive and required a lot of time and energy. Nonetheless, they were givers and went out of their way to help others, especially children. My mother was trying to figure out what to do with her life. She volunteered as a candy striper (nurse assistant) at the local hospital. Her supervisor bossed her around nonstop.

The job was nerve-wracking. She had little control of her

workday. There is research that show when people in subordinate roles and with low socioeconomic status perceived their jobs unfavorably it causes distress, resulting in poor mental and physical health. I understand now how those conditions stressed her out.

I shared a special bond with my mother, as all developing fetuses do. I felt her stress in the womb. And that same connection goes for other pregnant woman who have severe stress on the job, in relationships, and are frustrated with life. Their babies are in jeopardy too.

According to Daniel Keating, author of *Born Anxious*, some infants come into world born anxious because their mothers are stressed out during their pregnancies. My body in utero was exposed to high doses of my mother's stress hormones (primarily cortisol and adrenaline) that chemically changed the expression of my stress gene. That biological process is called epigenetics methylation.

The prefix Epi means above. Epigenetics is a new science that explains biologically how environmental influences such as severe job stress, conflict at home, financial pressures, or any chronic stressors can change gene expression. "An epigenetic change known as 'methylation'--named after methyl, that chemical compound that is responsible--shuts down a key gene that is designed to tell the stress system to turn off when a threat has passed. The result is stress dysregulation (SDR) that leads to an oversupply of stress hormone cortisol on a pretty constant basis."[4]

In this case, my mom's chronic stress and emotions of sadness, fear, frustration, and anxiety produced chemical (tags) methyl that attached to the stress gene, altering how it was expressed. Biologically it's what happens in many cases like mine, in which the mothers are

---

[4] Daniel Keating, Born Anxious: The Lifetime Impact of Early Life Adversity – and How to Break the Cycle, 2017, page 10.

chronically stressed during pregnancy. The mind and body (mind-body) are connected, what affects the mind (emotions) also is felt in the body. They work together to keep us alive and maintain our bodily functions. Stress is a natural phenomenon the mind-body manages efficiently under optimal conditions. Too much of anything (un-managed stress) for a prolonged period throws off the balance of the mind-body.

In this case it was a young pregnant mother's chronic distress causing her mind-body to adapt but in an unhealthy biological way to her stressed emotional state. As it relates to my mom, the mind-body during this complex process said your severe stress is overwhelming me, and there is a cost I must pay for your persistent stress. I must adapt to these stress chemicals that are surging through me, it's too much too handle. You're overwhelming me. I'm going to place a chemical price tag (methylation) on your stress gene and change how it's expressed. That's your cost for being severely stressed out. These tags are going to switch your stress gene off.

CHAPTER 3

How to Recognize
these Chemical Tags

Therefore, these chemicals tags are going to lock your stress gene in the off position for now. Your stress response will run nonstop.

Now you will react to the slightest of stressors in your environment in an abnormal and overreactive way to accommodate what you are accustomed to. You will be ready for anything coming your way. It's not good for your overall health in the long run, but for now you must adapt. When your stress level improves, I'll make some new chemical tags and modify the gene again and dial your stress dysregulation down to a more normal level.

Unfortunately, I must make the same changes in your fetus to because he must be ready for the same high levels of stress waiting for him in the outside world. Based on what you're going through, it's tough out here.

Please excuse my oversimplified way of explaining a complex biological process, but you get the point.

Connecting the dots for you – during your mother's pregnancy do you know what her stress level was?

Was her pregnancy peaceful or filled with dread and emotional uncertainty about her future?

Were her parents supportive, critical, punitive, indifferent or threatening?

How to Recognize these Chemical Tags

Was the person who fathered you kind to her, unkind, or indifferent?

Was she in a relationship with someone that didn't work out?

Did she have financial struggles and relational conflict?

Did she live in a place with a high rate of social stressors? The quality of those relationships and where and how she lived matters. There are countless adults who fetuses in the womb were affected by similar conditions or worse and are unaware of it. For example, toxic stress "occur when a child experiences strong, frequent, and/or prolonged adversity-such as physical or emotional abuse, chronic neglect, caregiver substance abuse or mental illness, exposure to violence, and/or the accumulated burdens of family economic hardship-without adequate adult support."[5] Without someone to buffer and help them feel secure and safe, Infant stress dysregulation can lead to adult mental and physical health problems.

---

[5] http://developingchild.harvard.edu/science/key-concepts/toxic-stress/

CHAPTER 4

A Broken Bond

A Parental Relationship Is Harmed

My mother told me after I was born, I had jaundice and had to stay in the hospital for several days to recover. No one visited me. I read an article online in the *Good Housekeeping* magazine about a so-called child expert in the 1960s who told parents not to hug or cuddle their babies because it would make them a socialist. In those days, not picking up crying babies right away was a common practice that was supposed to prevent parents from spoiling them. The thinking was if they were fed and changed, and they were still crying to let them cry it out; it was assumed their needs were met. We now know not responding to their cries stressed babies out and made them feel unwanted and unloved. My cousin Rhonda told me about the babies in our house were trained in this manner as they were in many homes in those days, because we were told it was best for them.

On the contrary, babies come into the world, needing to connect emotionally and physically with their mothers or mother figures; they need love. Particularly after birth, they need skin to skin contact with the mother and to be in her warm embrace, to hear her soothing voice (prosody), and to feel her heartbeat and be captivated by the glow in her eyes.

It's a biological necessity.

It calms the baby down and stimulates positive brain

development for social and emotional wellbeing. Many bonding chemicals in the brain, like dopamine and oxytocin, are stimulated by secure attachments. When this bonding does not take place, the baby's stress response is increased, stunting brain growth and impairing social and emotional development.

I wonder if I was held enough if at all during my hospitalization. When the attachment to the mother is interrupted by separation, or she is non-engaged because she is overwhelmed, emotionally worn out, or has mental health issues that make it hard for her to attune with her child, a breakdown in attachment occurs.

CHAPTER 5

Effects of the Separation

That time away from my mother after birth was traumatic for me. For example, my separation immediately after birth, to treat the jaundice my body was fighting, was a physical stressor and activated the stress response, because it was a threat to my survival. This kept the stress dysregulation going.

My mother worried about me when I was in the hospital. She loved me and wanted me home. But after I was discharged, she was doubtful. The reality of caring for me set in. I felt her ambivalence.

The mothering instinct is a strong drive, but chronic stress disrupts the best of intentions. When I looked into her eyes for comfort, unknowingly and unintentionally she communicated uncertainty (her nonverbal messages) i.e., her facial impression, posture, and her lack of emotional reciprocity conveyed doubt and fear. I felt unwanted, afraid, and unsafe. I encoded those negative emotions as an implicit memory.

I looked for acceptance via a secure attachment but felt an ambivalent attachment. I'm not blaming my mother, as she was unaware of this dynamic way back then.

Implicit memories are unconscious. As it relates to childhood trauma or toxic stress, we don't have any recollection of any experience before the age of 3-years-old because the experience occurred before the hippocampus and other related brain regions that hold explicit memories emerge. But other parts of our mind-bodies remember (primitive parts of our emotional brain called the amygdala, a part of the

Limbic system) is developed and stores those memories and the (body) nervous system.

My mind-body kept an unconscious record of those early life experiences (implicit memories) that often revisited me time and time again when stressful situations triggered them without understanding why until now. My mind-body went, oh I've felt this feeling of being unwanted and afraid before. I don't know when and where, but it feels familiar. I unconsciously (erroneously) perceived some disagreements or personal conflicts as rejection, or that I was personally being signaled out and mistreated because I was unworthy. I felt betrayed in relationships and was hurt deeply, to an intolerable level, over minor issues. I personalized it all. Something was wrong with me; I was not good enough, too flawed to be loved. Those identical feelings I felt after being born rejection. It provoked a lot of fear, stress, and anxiety, not knowing why.

A short time after, I came out of the hospital. My mother reluctantly decided to give me to family members in Pittsburgh, Pennsylvania that wanted a child. They scheduled a meeting for my mother to meet them to hand me over. She traveled to the city of bridges to give me away. She stayed with those relatives and prepared to turn me over to them.

Her conscious could not handle the thought of giving up her baby. In the quiet of night, she packed her bags and brought me home. Although she kept me, it caused her more stress. At that time, she was not ready to be a mother. She was still learning about herself and had dreams of becoming a nurse. I felt her uncertainty.

In chronically stressed babies, once the stress gene is switched off, it stays stuck in overdrive and different organs, such as the adrenal glands that sit on top of the kidneys, constantly release the stress hormones cortisol and adrenaline into their developing brains and bodies. In other words, the normal stress response system is broken.

Effects of the Separation

As a baby, I did not respond to stress in the normal way—my stress response did not adjust to stressors like it was supposed to. I startled easily, exhibited abnormal emotional and behavioral responses. I remember being an anxiety-stricken boy and young adult.

My aunt told me I was a colicky baby.

I was a highly sensitive baby who needed what prominent attachment researcher Dan Siegal calls super-nurturing during those stressful times but didn't get enough of it in ample doses. Babies and young children depend on their mothers, fathers, and other primary caretakers to be responsive to their needs to help them manage their emotions and stress. It takes many years for the executive functioning part of the brain to fully develop in the mid-twenties, until then children need adult nurturing and guidance.

It teaches babies to regulate. It is called co-regulation; babies, young children, teenagers, and even adults respond to it. I have the advantage now of education and hindsight to connect the dots for us. My mother did the best she could with what information and self-awareness she had at the time, as all mothers do. She was not mature enough to raise children.

During this crucial post-natal period, proper physical, emotional, and social engagement (attachment) makes the baby feel secure and safe, which are critical biological drives for a baby's survival. When I found out that my mother was close to giving me away, my anxiousness and fear in childhood made sense to me now. Why I was hypervigilant, and prone to anxiety disorders and depression. That revelation had confirmed my theory about attachment ruptures and the activation of the stress response.

My first reaction was unconscious (implicit memory). I felt discarded. I was hurt. Like I had a defect.

I had a lot of questions.

Why didn't she want me? What was wrong with me?

Effects of the Separation

Why didn't my grandmother take me?

She accepted my brother and cared for him. Why not me? Now, I am conscious of my implicit memory (attachment rupture and trauma) interference in my judgement related to challenges that I've had. I know what happened to both of us now. I empathized with my mother. I feel bad for her, young, confused, pregnant a second time, but not ready to have another child.

When I was two years old, my mother left for nursing school in Durham, North Carolina. I was separated again from her during crucial developmental years (5 years old and under), when attachment and bonding are needed the most.

My grandparents raised me. They were nurturing and supportive, but I wasn't the only child they parented. They cared for my brother, cousin, and many other children. Their love compensated for my mother and father's absence. During my early childhood years, it made the difference in my life. It's called allo-parenting.

I began to connect dots.

CHAPTER 6

A Stressed Community

I grew up in a poor and tough neighborhood in Washington, DC. My home was less than two miles from the White House and the US Capitol, long before the renewed cries for social justice and racial equity. In 1968, on the day that Martin Luther King, Jr. was killed, my older brother, Kelvin, remembered vividly playing football with neighborhood friends in a Church seminary's yard on the corner of our street on a patch of dirt.

Then a crowd of angry Black people took to the streets. Some pushed carts with ill-gotten gains, others rushed intently with the crowd, then a cloud of tear gas erupted. Choking, he ran home. Rioters then set fires and looted stores and businesses like the social unrest in 2020. It was a traumatic event.

The aftermath led to burnt-out stores, some deaths, ransacked buildings, and gutted houses. The mayhem destroyed parts of my city and many others around the country. Poverty made the conditions more stressful, a glaring reminder of the inequities in society. The unrelenting distress in the weeks, months, and years to follow lay bare the resilience and vulnerabilities of abandoned people. In 1972, Human Kindness Day was created to promote national togetherness and featured local and national artists on the National Mall. Some people, back in my neighborhood, overwhelmed by the social stressors (poverty, violence, drugs) acted aggressively and rebelliously and without agency succumbed to the stress.

I remember a group of neighborhood youth went to that event. Later it was rumored that one of them knocked a man's eye out. It was a horrific crime that made national news at the time considering the irony. The event ended in the spring of 1975, after the violence ruined the festivities.

Johann Hari, author of *Lost Connections*, traveled around the world and his research confirmed my belief and experience that when people feel disconnected, they are separated from our shared sense of meaning, which causes stress. Human beings are wired (neurologically) to feel safe together in a social group. It's the optimal environment for us to thrive and survive. Not having access to meaningful work, being separated from other people, disconnected from values, and excluded from achieving status and respect creates conditions for helplessness, which sowed the seeds for anxiety and depression.

It was no surprise a troubled youth (I wondered what his childhood was like) had lost his way and allegedly committed such a heinous crime. "Elijah Anderson, the sociologist, In the Code of the Street, has a persuasive explanation for the presumed deficiencies for such deviant behavior. Because inner-city youth were blocked from more traditional ways to succeed and achieve a meaningful identity, the violence and criminality that they engaged in were in fact adaptive in their circumstances-even if it ran against the mainstream norms." [6]

Like most grandparents, mine strove to heal those wounds and change that mentality. Their spiritual presence, support, and strength during those tumultuous times buffered many people, including me. The families that nurtured and showed up for their children, particularity during the bleakest of times, fostered resilience and hope. Their love and attention helped us to cope with the social stressors in the environment.

---

[6] Daniel Keating, Born Anxious: The Lifetime Impact of Early Life Adversity – and How to Break the Cycle, 2017, page 21.

Their recognition that we mattered lessened the likelihood that stress would overpower us. It is a form of attunement that all children and adults need.

Science shows that when an attachment ruptures, without any support (buffer) to offset those traumas, pain-based behaviors occur. In other words, some people act out abnormally, even aggressively and violently, when stressed.

In the US, and around the world, the opioid epidemic reflects a broader mental health crisis connected to a void of human attachment. People are hurting and do not feel acknowledged or loved, so they turn to drugs to alleviate their pain. When people are buffered from the ill effects of distress and trauma, they can transcend the harshest of conditions, they can break free from addictions, and pursue their dreams.

It's never too late to be buffered.

CHAPTER 7

Nurturing an Ailing Community

My grandfather, James, was the patriarch of the family. We didn't call him Papa or Grandpa, just James. He fed and kept a roof over the heads of fourteen people. He had a fourth-grade education. His father, Earnest Norman Webster, showed him how to be kind and resilient. "He raised four children after he lost his first wife. He survived World War I, the virus of 1918, the Great Depression, World War II, and the loss of his second wife while raising 13 children."[7] It was his transgenerational legacy. James's lack of book knowledge was surpassed by his empathy, kindness, and work ethic.

He never had a bad thing to say about anybody. He woke up at 5:00am every morning for work and he did that until he retired. He had great pride and his family and was a hard worker. He stocked heavy, gray, octagon-shaped metal film crates in a large warehouse for the defunct Clark Filming Company. They distributed movies to theatres, such as the holiday classic, *It's a Wonderful Life*, and he worked as the porter.

One perk of the job was free movie passes. He gave them to kids to escape the stress in our neighborhood, even if only temporarily. In DC, back in those days, we had three movie theatres on U Street: the

---

[7] Jackqueline Allen, decendent.

Republic, the Booker T, and the Lincoln Theater. Going to the movies transported us to another place and time. It was a great stress reducer.

Our imaginations enabled us to become the characters on the screen. We saw Shaft and Bruce Lee movies at the Lincoln Theatre. I remember many kids in the neighborhood making nun chucks and pretending to be Bruce Lee.

James was the father figure that I didn't have. He kept me close to him. I have fond memories of the time we spent together. He taught me the value of meaningful and hard work and the power of love. His love for me reinforced our attachment and strengthen my resilience. I saw his pride each day he went to work and had an opportunity to provide for his family.

He often took me to work with him. At his job, I looked forward to getting snacks from the snack jar. He had placed a small confection kiosk with multiple jars in the break room. The honors system was in force. If you took a snack, you had to leave the payment in a tin cup. The regular price was 5 cents; I got them for free. I had always wondered where those coins that jingled in his pocket came from. On numerous occasions when he gave me a quarter, he'd give my friends money too. I asked him, James why do you always give other kids money too? His response, I do not want them to feel any less important than you. They need to know someone cares. A lot of people are stressed out around here. I know their kids are stressed out too. He showed them empathy and compassion.

James knew even small acts of kindness were a currency that paid off in the lives of others, especially the children from hard places. The children and youth (achievers) who succeeded had someone positive in their lives who believed and supported them. He was like some other role models in my old neighborhood, who made a positive difference. They had a growth mindset. They were nurturers who instilled values, had integrity, and advocated for equality. They saw our potential. Even in the darkness, there was a spirit of hopefulness that some of us would make it out and some of us did, but not unscathed. Growing up in such a place even with buffers, the social conditions had lingering effects on us into adulthood.

CHAPTER 8

The Buffering Effect

James was a God-worshiping person. He prayed before every meal. A kind-hearted man with broad shoulders and strong arms, he did not look his age. He always had a smile and kind words to share. He loved helping people. There was an easygoing way when he walked. His demeanor exuded a worry-free attitude. Everybody on our street knew and liked him. He helped to build the first playground across the street from our house on a dirty sand lot.

He knew kids needed some place to play to act out their stress. It had a shiny steel sliding board (if you went down, it on a hot summer day, you burnt your skin), three swings, and a tunnel shaped like a stubby T, a Black cast iron industrial pipe, six-foot-long, with a wide mouth four-foot opening at each end and in the middle. I spent many days playing in that tunnel. I avoided it sometimes because it smelled like urine. I still have the Black and white faded picture of him standing next to it, wearing some dark khakis and a white T-shirt, smiling, be spackled with paint on his face with his eyeglasses perched on his wide nose holding a paintbrush.

He was a father figure and buffer for many fatherless boys and young men in our neighborhood; he steered them in the right direction. Often, he gave the last dollar in his pocket to others in need. At other times, his friendly personality and caring spirit drew people to him for support. He was there for people when they needed him the most. Whether it was a value passed down or his personality or a part of his faith, he showed others that he cared. It was his way of showing up for kids.

My grandmother, we called her Mama, was a homemaker. She helped raise multiple grandchildren, cared for other children in the neighborhood and helped others in need.

Of the kids in my family, I was handyman, Jr. I liked helping. I did it for the attention. I knew I could get her undivided attention helping her do jobs in the house that no one else did, like washing clothes. We had an old-fashioned white wringer washing machine. I would help roll it to the kitchen sink to use. When it was cut on, it made a loud rattling noise and vibrated.

I liked helping to wring out clothes and push them through the wringer. It set atop of the washing basin. It looked like two spinning dough rollers pressed together on top of each other, encased in a metal enclosure. I'd push wet laundry through the wringer, then reach around and catch it coming out on the other side. It was like playing a game to me. I was sure to catch them and not let them fall to floor. I piled the clothes up in my arms and hung them on a clothesline in our backyard with clothespins. Then I stood like a proud puppy, waiting for a response. When Mama smiled in approval. I felt special, if only at that time.

Mama was a loving person. Sometimes I thought my brother was her favorite, or at least that's what I perceived, even though that was not how she really felt. Mama treated all her grandchildren with same.

My implicit memory of my mother's ambivalence and lack of attachment was a constant (although unconscious) feeling of unworthiness of being loved, especially when I got into trouble. When I was punished for something, I never looked at what I did wrong. I blamed it on being the scapegoat. Somebody had to be blamed. The feeling of being the outcast was stored as an implicit memory. This feeling of inadequacy was stressful and caused a lot of anxiety for me. I was unaware of it at the time. It interfered with my family relationships, my friendships, my self-esteem, and even how I functioned in the broader society.

In that same backyard, my mother told me when I was five or six, I ate dirt by the spoonful, which made me cringe. I wondered who was watching me and why they let me.

Some may say children do foolish things like that, sometimes exploring through play. I have another theory. I ate non-nutritive substances because I had PICA. It's a psychological disorder in some children caused by various things and being distressed is one of them. Connecting the dots.

Mama was resilient. She had diabetes, but it did not stop her from living. It was something she had for a long time, along with anxiety. My cousin Rhonda told me her nerve pills, aka Valium, calmed her down. Her courage motivated us to persevere.

I often picked up her insulin at the drug store. I turned away when she gave herself shots. But it did not bother her; she had done it for so long. We saw syringes, half filled with blood on the street. They were called dope needles. We knew to stay away from them. In retrospect, those used needles represented how people self-medicated to avoid their pain. When Mama's purse was snatched one day coming from the grocery store, I was hurt.

The force slammed her frail body to the ground. I cried. The attacker's determination was evident by her severe bruises and bloody arms. We wondered who did it. Severe stress causes aggression in some people. Was it someone wanting money to get a fix? The pain did not break her spirit, though. My grandparents knew wounded people, hurt people. This desperate act was one of reasons why my grandparents helped people they wanted to change that behavior.

They aimed to make a positive difference. For example, they let a young mother and her two young children move into our house. The woman did not get along with her mother. And she was involved in a domestic violence situation that left her homeless. She ran errands for Mama. When her mother put her out, Mama could not stand to see her on the street with two young children. She moved her in our house. They became members of our family.

She later had three more children. We were a hodgepodge of people nurtured and sheltered by my grandparents, thankful for the opportunity to live in a loving family. Our house was a waystation for relatives, friends, and strangers who had fallen on hard times. During my childhood, many people lived with us. It was our tribe and my grandparents modeled charity, empathy, and togetherness.

CHAPTER 9

Our Home

Wherever we grew up, whether in a rural area or city, in a house or an apartment, on a farm or in a communal living arrangement or government subsidized housing, we remember that place, our home. Every room has a memory of shared experiences with family and friends that stay with us forever. My grandfather tried hard to keep up the property. He was always patching up holes, painting and repairing something. I was his apprentice. We had a big backyard and green metal garage that looked more like a shed, situated off the alley. I spent a lot of time playing in that garage.

My grandfather had a classic vintage Coca-Cola machine he salvaged from his job in there and an assortment of old tools and lumbar. I spent a lot of time playing and using my imagination. My neighbors' yard was overgrown with plants and bushes. I often went through the fence to catch insects, praying mantis, grasshoppers, and beetles. I was fascinated with insect and animal behavior and the environments in which they lived. I learned a lot about stress watching them.

I had a lot of pets growing up. One day my pet lizard lost part of his tail and stopped moving. We thought it had died. My cousin Johnathan tried to cremate it by setting it on fire with bicycle patch glue. It ran away. It wasn't dead.

According to Stephen Porges, reptiles that are stressed and cannot run or fight back become immobile (freeze) to survive, like what humans do in some cases during overwhelming stress they freeze too. They dissociate or become numb when they cannot escape or fight back. I had seen a lot of that in human behaviors in my old neighborhood too.

Our house was a four-story, battered, Victorian-style row house. Beneath the weathered and peeling paint and splintered hardwood floors was a relic of the bygone period of architectural beauty of the late 1800s. That is when the house was built. We had the most charming decorative plaster molding, accentuating the living and dining room with an ornamental medallion in the center of the ceiling.

In the foyer near the front door was a huge wooden frame mirror adorned with a fox head on top. I did not appreciate beauty until I grew older, and the house became mine.

Our house was attached to other's houses and rats and roaches often came through the walls. The flying cockroaches were hard to kill because they were fast and could fly. It was a constant battle to rid our house of them. We did not have them all the time. Do not take me wrong, our house was not dirty by no means; like everything else in the neighborhood, it was a causality of hardship. When new neighbors moved in and out of the rooming house next door, the rodents came through the walls. I spent many nights in combat.

When I was 10 years old, James sat me down at the kitchen table late one night and showed me how to set rat traps. I thought they only ate cheese, but I learned they'll eat almost anything. James' preferred bait was bacon. The texture of it was the right toughness to grab onto the bait bar. When rats pulled it, it tripped the kill bar. You had to have quick hands to set it, or you got your fingers popped. I sat so many traps I became proficient at it.

I hated those rats and roaches; they were worse than mosquitoes.

I learned a lot about stress from watching rats, like Hans Selye, the father of the stress movement. The rats that had near misses learned from their pain and avoided the traps. They figured it out—those strange contraptions can kill me.

They learned quickly how not to get caught in the traps. I had to find more creative ways to use the traps because the smart rats stopped going for them. So, I disguised the trap by placing it in the trashcan and camouflaging it with pieces of paper. It worked most of the time.

Like the rats, I quickly learned that in my neighborhood, making the wrong decision could get you killed.

In my preteens, I had an encounter with a rat one day in the summer in my backyard. It taught me a valuable lesson about the stress response. I had grabbed a big stick in chased it into a corner outside my back door. It was big and had the longest tail, which looked like a gray frayed wire. Young and dumb, I approached the angry creature. It was frightened. It hunched its back and squealed menacingly. It gave me the signs that it felt threatened and that I had better back off.

I didn't pick up on its fight or flight or freeze response. Out of nowhere, it jumped straight at me, toward my face. Instinctively, I twisted my body like I was in the matrix movie in moved out of its way. Later, my grandfather told me not to ever corner an animal because they will fight back, classic stress response. No different from human beings.

At an early age, to survive harsh conditions and to overcome stress, just like the smallest of creatures, I had to learn from my mistakes, avoid dangerous places, and fight back if necessary. I discovered new ways to adapt to my changing environment like those rats. It was vital to my survival. It would be the key to my success.

CHAPTER 10

Q Street, Living in
a Stressed Culture

Gabor Mate, an acclaimed retired Canadian physician, and author of *In the Realm of Hungry Ghost: Close Encounters with Addiction,* says childhood traumas and parenting ruptures in attachment have had a detrimental impact on many unaware people who are dealing with adult mental and physical health problems. I have experienced many people affected by childhood adversity and trauma demonstrate maladaptive behaviors that make his point.

I lived on Q Street as a child. Back then, to outsiders it was known for prostitution, drugs, and crime. But it was where we lived; it was our home.

The ladies (girls and women) of the night were common fixtures in the neighborhood. Tragically, they were sex trafficked. Their lives mattered though; they were someone's daughters, sisters, aunts, mothers, nieces, and friends. I could only wonder what awful circumstances led them here.

My training in social work has taught me that childhood adversity and trauma are major factors that make people vulnerable to exploitation. Perhaps a combination of unfortunate events such as severed family relationships, being sexually abused and neglected left them disoriented, traumatized, and loss.

In search of acceptance and love, seeking safety, instead they were manipulated, exploited, and re-traumatized. Who knows what adverse childhood experiences they went through?

As a child, I saw more illicit sex acts than I should admit. Sometimes, I would walk around the corner and right there in broad daylight someone was having sex. I lost my sexual innocence witnessing those illicit sex acts. Used condoms were strewn around our neighborhood, amongst liquor bottles, broken glass, and other trash. It was a depressing sight.

On the corner of Q Street, not even a block away from my house, was a methadone clinic where crowds of substance abusers often lined up for their medicine. The large crowds that waited showed the magnitude of chronic stress and trauma. I often saw people standing in line with swollen hands and abscesses; some of them nodded back and forth.

I knew what that meant. They were heroin addicts who comforted themselves by wrapping their arms tightly with anything to expose a vein to inject heroin. Sometimes they put the needle anywhere they could find a good vein. Their addiction was a temporary escape from their distress. It was the only pain killer they knew. Their behavior showed how emotional scars are hard to heal, and that emotional suffering can lead to addictions.

On the street, they had derogatory names for people like that. They were called dope fiends. This insensitivity to human suffering reflected their ignorance of toxic stress. As a social worker, I wish I could go back in time. I would provide therapy and help them identify the source of their pain. When those ghosts are dealt with appropriately in therapy or through some other form or counseling, an emotional breakthrough can occur, and they would be set free.

There are lessons in their suffering. We have unfortunate, horrific, and even traumatic events happen to us and holding on to shame and guilt has a way of destroying our lives. We self-medicate and have addictions of all kinds to mask our anxiety and depression. It stays with us in our bodies and is hard to let go but let go of it we must. Start a new, learn from your experiences, forgive those who have hurt you, get help to be free of your past trauma.

CHAPTER 11

A Lost Child

To escape the stress of the neighborhood, on Friday evenings, James grabbed his cap, jacket, and put his newspaper under his arm and a cigar in his mouth. This was how he prepared for his favorite outing, going to Rosecroft or Laurel horse racetracks in Prince George's County, Maryland. He loved to watch the horses run. He hardly ever won any money. Sometimes he went with $20 in his pocket. I do not remember him ever smoking the cigars. Most of the time he just chewed them. Occasionally my grandmother went; she always won. James could not figure that out. Sometimes he asked me to pick a horse. They had weird names.

I went to the racetrack with him a lot over the years until I became a teenager. I had watched people's odd behaviors. The excitement on their faces from the adrenaline rush they got betting on a horse and then the depression they felt when they lost their money. Sometimes I sat in the stands with James and thought about the time when I got lost at the racetrack.

I was seven years old and had wandered off. A police officer saw me and picked me up. I am glad he found me before a pedophile did. He asked me my name, and I said, Mr. Darryl. He announced on their loudspeaker that a child named Mr. Darryl had been found. I was always wandering off, easily distracted, hyperactive, inattentive, and got into mischief.

I am certain I had Attention Deficit Hyperactivity Disorder

(ADHD), a symptom of stress.

Later, James bought me a small tan wooden folding stool to celebrate my being found and returned. He wrote my name on it in big Black letters, MR DARRYL. He told me in an affectionate voice with a laugh, "when we are at the track, this is your chair. See your name, stay on it, sit still."

Like a lost and wandering child at the racetrack, life is confusing at times; stress takes us off course, and we get lost. We go astray and make mistakes and need someone or something to guide us to safety. We must sit down, be still, and find time to meditate and bring calmness to our minds and bodies. It is one way to transcend feeling lost and hopeless.

CHAPTER 12

The Good Stress

Eustress is the opposite of distress. It is the type of good stress that we enjoy, that makes us happy, that challenges us, that stretches our minds and bodies to grow. For me, on summer days I played hopscotch outside. The girls jumped rope (double Dutch) and we all played dodgeball, hot bread and butter, jacks, basketball, and tackle football. At night we sat outside on the front stoop and watched the craziness taking place on our street. We did not have air conditioning and television programming went off at midnight.

As kids, we had a keen sense of situational awareness. I was hypervigilant. The code of the street was mind your business and run home if you felt threatened. Obviously, it was not the best environment to raise kids or live in, but when you are poor and housing is inexpensive, you lived where you could afford it.

Holidays were stressful, the positive kind, and fun, with gifts and toys under the tree. Everyone in the house pitched in. James kept the Christmas lights tucked away in his closet in the basement. I loved that time of the year. I helped him hang the lights around our windows. Everything seemed brighter. But even during these times I periodically felt sad, but didn't know why.

My low mood made the holiday season a time of ambivalence. I did not know what it was or how to talk about it. In those days mental health issues were not talked about.

The whole family helped decorate the tree. We had two trees.

The one in the basement was for the toys. In the living room was a big, live tree for the presents. People checked out their gifts before Christmas day, trying to figure out what is in them. I did odd jobs in the neighborhood, shoveled snow, pumped gas, ran errands, anything to make money to buy my grandparents presents.

I gave James a box of El product cigars and Mama perfume. I wrapped them up in colorful decorative wrapping paper and put a bow on them. My wrapping skills had a lot to be desired, but it was the thought that counted. On Sundays, Mama cooked dinner. The family came together as one. I loved when she cooked sweet potatoes, rice, collard greens, and chicken. Those were the best days of my childhood, having fun, spending time with family. It was those experiences that helped me grow up with self-awareness, good social and emotional skills, and secure.

CHAPTER 13

Childhood Trauma

What memories do you have of your childhood? Do they put a smile on your face or make you angry or sad, or do you feel a range of emotions? Or are they a mixture of cloudy fragments of events you lost contact with a long time ago? If you could tag those memories, what emotional tag would you place on them? Happy, sad, angry, bitter, and depressed. How have they shaped who you are? Do you harbor a family secret that you have never told anyone about because it's too painful to talk about? Has it been stressful for you reliving past trauma you cannot seem to let go of and cannot stop thinking about? They have led to anxiety disorders and depression. Reminiscent of the crowds of people standing in line at the methadone clinic in my old neighborhood, have you masked your emotions by self-medicating, fallen in deep despair, rumination, and pain?

My brother Kelvin's and my best childhood friends died young. They were the same ages as us. Kermit, the younger one, was my age. We were close friends until the age of thirteen, when I started playing organized basketball. Walter was my brother's age. He and Kelvin stayed close friends throughout high school. They both lived in our neighborhood. I spoke with Walter before his death. He shared his story. He said, "Me and my brother did not have a chance for a good life because of what happened to us as children. Our lives were never ending stress."

He added, "My father was a raging alcoholic who beat my

mother, me, and my brother constantly. We were hostages in our home. He frequently attacked us during his drunken fury. He kept a lot of knives on him and spent hours in our backyard throwing them at trees. We were in constant fear that if we made him mad, he might stab us. We were afraid of him most the time. And to witness our poor mother go through that hell was even more terrifying and sad."

"He was bigger than life in the worse way. We were defenseless against him because he was so much bigger and stronger than us. We could not do anything to stop his abuse, especially when we were young. He was an emotionally sick man. His made us feel hopeless. Kermit had difficulty controlling his bowels as a child. He frequently defecated on himself. He got teased and bullied about it."

I feel great sadness looking back, understanding what they were going through in their house. Then to have neighborhood kids tease you about it had to be emotionally devastating. I believe he had encopresis caused by the emotional and physical abuse his father put him through.

Both men struggled in their lives. They never broke away from their childhood trauma; they could not adapt. It was not their faults though. They were wonderful human beings, kind, friendly. I had fun playing with them growing up as kids. It was the impact of the childhood adversity and trauma that ruined their lives.

Now I get why they spent so much time at our house. Kermit often got into trouble with the law. He started using drugs and became addicted and could not get his life together. I later learned he had gotten married, and it seemed he was trying to rebuild his life. But he died in his early forties.

His brother would live a decade longer but died in his fifties. He told me, "Darryl, I have had high blood pressure for years, been on dialysis, have had diabetes, and other health complications most of my adulthood." He added, "It's been rough for me." Our childhood friends' lives were cut short. It demonstrated the seriousness of adverse childhood experiences and the impact of complex trauma on the developing brain and body of children.

Childhood trauma does alter the stress genes, activating the stress response making victims vulnerable to mental and physical health issues later in adulthood, especially if you do not have support or a person to buffer you. Even with a buffer, if you are out of control and not listening to the person who is trying to help you, that behavior could lead to self-destruction.

I only wished our friends could have gotten the help he and his brother needed to process their traumas and heal their wounds.

As a child, I did not know the severity and depth of our friends' toxic stress and trauma. Their story was tragic and reminded me of the ACE's research. That childhood trauma and adversity change human biology. Bessel Van Der Kolk, a leading psychiatrist, researcher, and expert on trauma talks about it in his best-selling book, *The Body Keeps the Score*.

Our childhood friends are classic examples of the damaging impact of childhood adversity and its lifelong impact on social relationships, substance abuse and addiction, criminality, poor physical and mental health outcomes. Our friends were good people that bad things happened to them to no fault of their own.

Both brothers suffered at the hands of their father and exposure to domestic violence and no telling what else went on in their house. If you are the victim of childhood adversity and trauma, please seek help. It's not your fault what happened to you. There are lots of great resources to heal yourself. Bibliotherapy is an inexpensive way to start the healing process. If you are a member of a religious organization, i.e., church, synagogue, mosque, reach out to the minister, rabbi, or imam or whoever leads your religious congregation. Additionally, there are hundreds of other therapeutic services are available to you. Please take advantage of them.

CHAPTER 14

Overcoming Despair

When I was 12 years old, my friend George's father died of suicide. The sadness and grief his family went through was agonizing to watch. I felt bad for him, for his brothers and sisters, and mother. The thought that they would never see him again scared me. It was if my family member had died. I had met his father many times, been in their house around him, and never saw any signs of mental illness.

Nor did George ever talk about his father having an issue. I was in shock for days and weeks after it happened. It made me depressed. I started thinking about how fleeting life is. I had deep thoughts about the meaning of life. I got fixated on death. My highly sensitive personality felt their pain deeply. When other kids went out to play, I found myself constantly thinking about George's father's death. It was upsetting.

Although my friend George did not talk about his father's suicide, I noticed his attitude and behavior changed. He was not as friendly; he did not come around in the neighborhood as much to play and started getting in trouble. Suicide death is tragic enough that the deceased ended their life. Then the repercussions for the remaining family and friends who are left behind to grieve, to make sense of it, are painful. So many emotions to sort out guilt, regret of not being there to help, and sorrow. If only they knew something was wrong or were able to stop them. If they could have them back in their lives just one more time, they would tell them how much they are loved. They would tell them not to give up, no matter how much the pain hurts, they would get through it together and things would get better, and that life is worth living.

If you are struggling emotionally and have psychological pain, do not keep it to yourself, regardless of how embarrassing or unmanageable you think your problem is. Talk to someone or a trained mental health professional who can offer sound and safe guidance.

A highly stressed mind is a poor decision maker. Don't self-medicate using drugs or alcohol or participate in a self-destructive behavior for a momentary escape or avoidance from the pain. If you are using drugs, alcohol, or engaged in any addictive behavior, it's only going to make things worse. Addictive behavior will cloud your thinking, leading to an irrational or tragic decision. Furthermore, the issue or problem that is the source of your pain is still going to be there when the substance wears off and the temporary pleasurable behavior is stopped, and in the long term your issue will get worse.

When we are overwhelmed, our emotional brain is reactive, and it takes over our thinking. Its purpose is to protect us from harm by sending chemical messages to other parts of our brain to sound the alarm that we are in danger. That initial alert sets a chain of reactions in place that activate the fight or flight or freeze response in action. Just our perceptions of fear and worry can frazzle our emotional brain. Chronic worry makes life more stressful and leads to anxiety and being depressed. When we are in this state, our decision making and problem-solving ability do not work as well.

It doesn't distinguish between if our thoughts are reality based or our imaginations running wild. The amygdala hijacks the part of our brains called the executive functioning, which is responsible for decision making, planning, judgement, foresights, self-regulation, and thinking flexibility.

The amygdala is running the show. Its purpose is to alert us to threats and to get us out of harm's way. A depressed and traumatized mind can feel dissociated, detached, and numb. The emotional pain is intolerable. When panic occurs, we think we are going crazy.

Finding a trusted person who can support and make you feel safe, the relationship will lessen your stress level, they can help you co-regulate as you struggle to find yourself in a dark place. If you don't have anyone you trust, contact a trained professional. They can help you in many ways. If you are having an emergency right now, call the national suicide prevention lifeline at 1-800-273-8255. It's free, and someone is on call 24/7.

First, talking it out will help you get some perspective about your problem. Second, do not catastrophize, in other words think the worst about your situation it only makes matters more complicated.

When I was younger, I did not understand how stress triggered anxiety and depression. Some people are vulnerable to mental illness and suicide because they try to manage their pain by themselves. It made me wonder if my grandfather ever thought about giving up on life. He was the breadwinner. He had a lot of pressure on him.

My grandfather's faith in God, his altruistic nature, and commitment to family and public service gave him the strength to persevere. I have learned not everybody who commits death by suicide has a mental illness. Sometimes it is an impulsive, desperate act. Done quickly, with no regard to those left behind. Now, I am more aware of the risk factors involved in psychological pain such as stressful life conditions. I have gotten through it and know life can be better. Do not use a permanent solution to solve a temporary problem. Get Help.

CHAPTER 15

Fatherlessness

According to a Blog, A Father's Impact on Child Development children without fathers in their lives are poorer, more likely to use drugs and alcohol, fail in school, and experience mental health and other emotional problems.[8] James was the only father I knew. But he was not my biological father. He was a surrogate, though an amazing one indeed. I tell people I had the best father a boy could have had. He loved me, and I knew it. He had a habit when he came home from work of hugging me or gently tugging at my ear or neck in an affectionate way and saying something kind. He did not need a textbook to know how to be a father. He either learned from his dad or had that special nurturing gift. Either way, he was the best at it.

I had to know who my biological father was.

My brother had his father in his life; why not me? I asked my mother who my biological father was. She told me. I contacted him. I visited him a few times; he was nothing like my grandfather. He was aloof, serious, and unaffectionate. He did not make any efforts to build a relationship with me. He was married and had three children.

I was told he won the Maryland Lottery in the late 1970s for a small sum. Then he moved to the suburbs. I discovered he was a foster

---

[8] Children's Bureau: https://www.all4kids.org/news/blog/a-fathers-impact-on-child-development/ 6/7/2018

child, and he had other children that he did not know. My theory was he had some bitterness toward his parents, who abandoned him. In turn, his life was a struggle, and no one was there to love and guide him. As a result, he did not know how to give something to his children that he never received, or perhaps something happened between my mother and him that he never got over. As human we make mistakes. We must learn to forgive people who have hurt us. It is the best way to destress your mind and body.

Forgiveness is not for the person who hurt you; it is for your health benefit. A few years ago, my sister on my father's side called and told me our father had died. I felt more sorrow for her and my other siblings than anything else. I had never had a relationship with my biological father; therefore, I did not know him or had no emotional connection to him and anyway.

But as time went by, I felt some regret not taking the initiative to get to know him. I felt I had missed an opportunity to understand the man and his motives for not getting to know me, to build a father/son relationship. In retrospect, even though he showed no interest, I should have been the bigger. more mature person and given it a shot to know him.

Maybe getting to know him would have shed some light on why he was like that and what happened in his childhood that guided his behavior. I could have learned some things about his past that could help me connect the dots about him. That insight may have revealed why his and my mother's relationship failed.

If you are in a similar circumstance and your father or mother is still living and you have an opportunity, communicate with them safely. Do it. If you are not ready, I understand. It is a hard decision to make. Everybody's situation is different. You may view your father's lack of accountability as unforgivable because he has hurt you. If your situation is reconcilable, it might bring you some solace or provide an explanation for his behavior that at least answer some questions you've always had. There are many reasons why relationships don't work. People fail to live up to their responsibility. Hidden traumas in people's lives they don't recognize are relived and acted out unknowingly in their relationships. At least hearing your dad out might lead to the both of you getting counseling and therapy to make sense of what happened. We don't know what we don't know, and sometimes we need professionals to connect the dots for us.

Having closure has its benefits. Who knows, you and your dad might hit it off. You might develop a sustained relationship and make up for lost time? I missed my opportunity to do so. Do not miss yours.

CHAPTER 16

Facing My Fear

One Sunday afternoon in the summer, Henry came to pick up Kelvin and Walter to take them to his boat. He loved being on the water. It was a great way to destress. I was around 9 years old. They told Henry not to bring me. Maybe he should have listened to them. But he brought me anyway. His boat, named *Christy*, was docked on the Potomac River near the Pentagon in Arlington, Virginia.

We arrived at the boat; it was a beautiful day. A cool breeze gently moved the through the air near the water. From the dock, we climbed over the back of the boat. Henry told us to stay where we were, then he went below deck. Kelvin and Walter left me. They told me to stay seated. They jumped up on the gunwale, which is the upper edge of the boat, grabbed hold of a railing, and side-stepped their way to the bow. I was an impulsive child, so I tried to follow them. I lost my footing and fell in the water. I could not swim.

Frantically, I flailed my arms, thrashing in the water as I tried to stay afloat. I was drowning and could not call for help. Henry heard the loud splashing water and thought it was ducks. He had fed them for years. They had been conditioned the same as Pavlov's dogs. When they splashed the water, he fed them. By divine intervention, he grabbed his duck food and went above deck to feed them. He was shocked; I was going under for the last time. Without hesitation, he dove in and saved me. I went home looking pitiful, wearing oversized clothes that Henry had on the boat.

Facing My Fear

I felt embarrassed, confused, and didn't know the seriousness of my near fatal drowning. I developed a phobia of water.

Kelvin later taught me how to swim. I remember the first time he made me jump off an 8-foot-high diving board. He waited at the bottom of the ladder and encouraged me to try. I was trembling. He said, do not be afraid. I will be in the water waiting for you after you jump. I slowly climbed the ladder to the top and walked out halfway on the platform. At first, I turned around and made my way down the ladder.

Kelvin told me I could do it. His presence and reassurance that I would be okay motivated me to try again. It was moments like that I felt close to my brother.

I went back up and walked to the edge. Kelvin was floating, waiting in the water below.

He yelled, "Jump, Darryl." I closed my eyes, grabbed my nose, and stepped off the diving board. When I hit the water, he grabbed me. He swam beside me to the edge of the pool.

CHAPTER 17

Sibling Rivalry

Kelvin and I are three years apart. We have different dads. He had a connection with his father. I did not have my father in my life. I envied their relationship. It was stressful seeing them together laughing and going on outings.

When Henry came around, it was a constant reminder that I did not matter to my biological father. His father was successful and handsome, standing 6'2", and had a perm like the singers from Motown. He owned a clothing cleaners' business, some apartment buildings, and a boat. He gave money to my grandmother for Kelvin. I noticed that.

Occasionally, Henry drove us in his shiny blue Cadillac convertible to the Shoney's Big Boy for ice cream. My favorite was hot fudge cake. Sometimes we stopped by Ben's Chili Bowl for a half smoke. I was happy when I got to go with them. When he did not take me, I felt like the ugly stepchild.

I did not know who my dad was earlier in my life. I envied Kelvin. I felt sad I did not have a father. Kelvin was chosen to be in a neighborhood movie. He was a star. James tried to make up for the father I didn't have. He gave me more attention than the other children in the house, or at least it felt that way to me.

Our personalities were different. I was sensitive, anxious, impulsive, hyperactive, and moody. Kelvin was outgoing, athletic, social able and handsome. When we were younger, sometimes we played together at home, along with our cousin Bob and the other kids in the house.

As we got older, we had different friends our age.

As I got older, I became interested in sports. I practiced a lot. We shared a brotherly love, but in a weird way. I was jealous of him. Outside the house, he went his way, and I went mine.

Around 15 years old, I had developed into a talented basketball player. I often played Kelvin one-on-one. Our games were highly competitive and stressful. It was personal to me. At least I could beat him at something, I thought. Although he was older, I had caught up with him talent-wise, and he did not like it. And when I played him, I tried my best to beat the crap out of him. I made a statement, trying to punish him for everything he had that I did not. At first, when I started beating him, he could not accept it. We fought.

CHAPTER 18

Bullied, A Loss of Control

I still remember the bullies in my childhood. Kids back then in my neighborhood enjoyed making fun, teasing, and name-calling, aka Joning on each other. I often felt embarrassed and humiliated when I got Jon on. It was a form of bullying. There was one boy, an older kid, who lived a few blocks from me. He'd beat me up on a regular basis and take my McDonald's money. I was terrified of him.

He came from a dysfunctional family, and it seemed all the kids in his house were bad people, even the girls. I never told anybody about him because I was too ashamed. Feeling helpless in any situation is not good. Our mind-body craves stability and certainty. When we are afraid of something, or someone in the case of a bully, we suffer emotionally and physically.

Bullies are menaces to society who hurt and terrorize people. In the eye of a victim, they may seem powerful and strong, but in essence they are weak and sad people. They bully others for many reasons. In some cases, we do not have to go far from home to find them. In some unfortunate cases, they are our parents, friends, family members, boyfriends, girlfriends, and spouses. Their belittling, taunting, ridiculing, and even physical attacks are painful. They cause emotional and physical scars.

Victims of bullies often suffer in silence from anguish, guilt, and shame. Have you carried with you years of bad memories still harboring the self-doubt, and poor self-image caused by being bullied? Do not let your bully define you. You are not the problem; they are. When we do not feel safe or are being threatened or in a bad relationship, biologically our bodies and minds are sieged by stress.

Some people are more resilient; they bounce back stronger after being bullied. Others feel defenseless. Their self-concept has eroded personal growth. As adults, some of us still harbor the trauma related to those experiences. In some relationships, people manipulate others to control and make them submissive. They play mental games to get the upper hand in the dysfunctional relationship. Be aware of the signs, such as the partner not sharing their emotions and intentionally not listening to get in your head, these people are master manipulators.

They know the person will respond with compliance. Other methods are acting like they don't remember something they remember playing games with someone's mind, in other words to make them think they are crazy: classic gaslighting. Conversations are one-sided, the victim is not allowed to have a voice, and when they do bring up something important, the perpetrator switches the topic.

Being in these types of relationships is a great source of stress, anxiety, and depression. You may feel helpless. Dealing with this nonsense day in day out is constantly activating your stress response, raising your heart rate, making you nervous, anxious, depressed, and a host of other emotional and physical symptoms associated with stress.

Please find someone to talk to who can help you figure out how to address this situation. You deserve better.

CHAPTER 19

Time to Heal

Some of us have not spoken to family members or friends in years because of past transgressions. We harbor destructive emotions: anger, guilt, disgust, shame, embarrassment, hate, or sadness, to name a few. The memories remain connected to their unfairness and meanness. I understand how childhood trauma is acted out in many cases of human misery and dysfunction. Perhaps a trusted person, or family member hurt you in the worst way. Those memories are embedded in the mind and body and may require counseling and even therapy to address it. There are a variety of therapy interventions that are evidenced based to help people work through their problems.

My childhood adversity and attachment ruptures contributed to my stress reactivity. In the past, I had avoided and held grudges against people who I perceived were unfair to me, betrayed me, and hurt me. I felt their betrayal deeply. I severed all ties and relationships with them.

I've been able to connect the dots.

Show yourself some grace and forgive yourself, and them, while you're at it. It will take a lot of stress off you. I have learned that constantly thinking about and reliving the hurtful memories of past events over and over in my mind every day, for weeks, and months, and even years has only reinforced the ordeal and kept those unfortunate memories alive in the present as if they are still happening. Each hurtful memory held onto is a dagger to the heart emotionally.

The more we think and behave a certain way, the more we are

strengthening those patterns of habit, making it harder to extinguish or vanished them from our minds. We keep ourselves in an emotional prison of victimhood.

Why focus on the past transgressions when there is nothing that can be done to change them? Get help and move on with your life in the present moment. I know it's hard to let go of past hurtful experiences. Focusing on the trouble seems justified because of the pain involved. And trauma does change who we are and how we view life. That's why therapy is needed in many cases when we are stuck in this vicious cycle.

We ruminate and worry, incessantly replaying past unhelpful scenes of being hurt. That harmful pattern of thinking has become an unhealthy feedback loop that has our nervous systems running nonstop in fight or flight or freeze mode outside of our awareness.

In some cases, it causes us to self-medicate with different types of inappropriate things, such as illegal drugs, opioids, sex, alcohol, and gambling. We try to numb ourselves to the discomfort, but in doing so we only prolonged the pain, because when the smoke clears and the high goes away, we realize we have made things worse.

Eckhart Tolle responded to a man during one of his talks on letting go of the past. The man had mentioned he occasionally would revisit memories of painful events to track his progress. Eckhart said "some reflection of past may be helpful depending on the context of how it is explored. But reliving the past hurt, whether you caused it, or it involves someone who hurt you, can be detrimental because going back to traumatic memories and rehashing what happened without resolving it is a form of suffering."

He added, we only have the present moment; it's the only time that matters.

CHAPTER 20

Some of Us are Born
Highly Sensitive

As a child, I am convinced I had an undiagnosed anxiety disorder. When I look back, I was a highly sensitive child. I recently confirmed something that I had suspected for years. I have a sensitivity gene. I read Elaine N. Aron, author of *The Highly Sensitive Person*, years ago. She estimates that 20 percent of the human population are highly sensitive. She says the trait is found in 100 species. In one of her talks on YouTube, she looked at HSP's brains in a FMRI machine and noticed HSP's have a depth of processing and feelings that non HSP's don't have. She says there are equal numbers of HSP men as women, but they hide it for obvious reasons. The main features of sensitive people are they are highly observant, easily over-stimulated, emotionally reactive, and empathic.

I like the way Elena Herdieckerhoff, a self-proclaimed HSP, describe what's it's like to be an HSP in her TEDx IHEP Paris talk. She says, "imagine living with your senses on high alert, where your emotions are magnified, sadness is deep sorrow, and joy is pure ecstasy, you also care beyond reason, and empathize without limits." This trait has helped me to be a responsive and loving father, husband, and social worker. But the downside is the unnecessary worry and sadness I've felt over the years working with and worrying about some children and parents at high-poverty schools.

Some of Us are Born Highly Sensitive

Tom Boyce, a renowned child psychologist, wrote a book title *The Orchid and Dandelion* that describes two types of children. Highly Sensitive Children are orchids and dandelions are the children who have an ability to grow and flourish in any condition. The orchids, due to their genetic susceptibility, require optimal parenting and social environment to blossom.

His research hit home for me. Orchid kids who are exposed to stressful conditions become highly reactive to their environments. They fare far worse than the dandelions. My brother Kelvin was a true dandelion. Nothing seems to get under his skin. Boyce's research showed that orchid children raised in harsh family and social environments or in my case infants with attachments ruptures can experience psychological and emotional struggles.

On the other hand, orchid children thrive and excel beyond the dandelions when they are raised by attuned parents in a loving and enriched environments where secure emotional attachments are established. When my mother returned from nursing college, she had matured and began repairing the ruptured attachment with me. But those first five years of attachment ruptures had taken a toll.

I feared watching scary movies, going to bed in the dark, someone breaking into our house, the world coming to an end over nuclear war, and my grandparents dying. I worried about everything and did not know why (also known as generalized anxiety disorder). I didn't know my temperament and personality was a complex mixture of a sensitivity gene, social/environmental influences, shaped by the attachment ruptures. This was a perfect storm that converged that shaped how I reacted abnormally to certain situations, events, and experiences. It makes sense now. I took one of the sensitivity gene test 5:HTTLPR (aka the serotonin transporter gene). I tested positive. Connecting the dots.

As a preteen, I feared going to sleep for a period. When I went to sleep, I'd have times when it felt like I was awake but could not move or talk. I felt paralyzed. I'd felt like a mysterious force was holding me down. It scared me so badly. I mentioned this experience to my young daughter. She responded, causally, that's called sleep paralysis; some of my friends have experienced it.

I was surprised. It's caused by many things, and stress and panic disorders are among them. Some of us are born highly sensitive to stuff which causes us to be anxious and makes us susceptible to stressful experiences. Our upbringing played a role in how our genes have been expressed without us even being aware of it.

I identified with this trait personally. It was a main feature of my personality growing up, which caused me angst. My grandparents compensated for what I didn't get at the start of my life. Their love and buffering helped me to bounce back from early life attachment ruptures and my innate sensitivity. If you suspect you have the sensitivity gene, there are various genetic testing companies that offer testing. I've learned there are great advantages of being an HSP.

CHAPTER 21

Homesick

One summer, my brother Kelvin and Cousin Joe went to camp. They returned to hugs and a hero's welcome. I could not wait for the next summer when I was old enough to go. They seemed to have had so much fun. At 10 years old, I joined them the following season. I excitedly packed my sleeping bag, mosquito spray, and flashlight. Off I went for a two-week journey with my brother and cousin. I eagerly went away from home on my first camping trip into the woods.

We arrived at the camp in the afternoon. It was beautiful, manicured grass fields as far as the eye could see, log cabins, and in the foreground a densely wooded area. The smell of pine trees filled the air and dew glistened on the wildflowers everywhere. It was such an idyllic-looking place. It was a picture out of a nature magazine.

I got off the bus, and camp staff separated us by age. I wasn't expecting that. My brother and cousin went with the older boys. I was escorted with my age group. My counselor was not nice. He told us the camp rules. On day one, I missed my grandparents and brother already.

The sunset and night drew near, and my anxiety and fear intensified. I sat by a campfire with a dozen little wide-eyed pre-adolescent boys who were eager to hear ghost tales. But not me. The counselors told frightening stories about Old Man Clutch, who lived in the woods. He came out at night to haunt kids. I was terrified. This nightly practice went on throughout the week. What was I thinking, wanting to come to a place like this and be traumatized?

This was not the perception of the camp that I had when my brother and cousin returned home the previous summer. What made them so different from me? Why didn't the separation from our grandparents make them feel sad? What weren't they frightened by the stories?

I should have known better; my brother would watch gruesome movies for fun. It did not bother him; it was entertainment. He could watch a horror film marathon and go to bed with a smile. Nope, I could not do that. My personality was sensitive. And I have an inventive imagination. I guess the camp counselors thought it was funny, but for me it was child emotional abuse. I did not want any part of it. I wanted to go home.

I was scared and didn't want to stay until the end. I was given a nickname, "homesick," and teased for being afraid. I do not remember anyone responding to my fears. The camp creed was to be tough and stick it out. I guess they figured they were making a man out of us. Wrong. For me, it was traumatizing every day.

There was a final night tradition: we had to stay in an abandoned house in the woods, or at least that's how they portrayed it. It sat on a cliff overlooking a huge body of water. The counselors set the ghastly tone by telling us it was haunted. On the last day, we trekked through the woods to the haunted house. I think this was our indoctrination into becoming brave and overcoming our fears. In retrospect, it was child abuse for kids like me.

The house was made to look like a haunted house, minus the crazy man with the chain saw. We cleaned up the house and prepared to make it through the night. We made a fire in the fireplace, roasted marshmallows, and began telling ghost stories. I remember tucking myself into my sleeping bag like a turtle with his head withdrawn. Then I stuck my hand out and zipped myself up so tight, no one could see me, especially Old Man Clutch, if he happened to come by.

I have enough space now to breathe out. It was one of the longest nights of my life. The noises of the night woods kept me up. My over-active imagination was running wild. Occasionally, I pulled my zipper down low enough to peek out and to see what was going on. The other campers were sound asleep, along with the counselors. I barely survived the night. It was very traumatic for me.

That type of camp experience was not for me. When I returned home, I was ecstatic to see and be with my grandparents and other family members. I felt like I was released from a prison. No more summer camps in the woods for me. Fortunately, there was an organization in my neighborhood that had year-round activities and a summer program that was fun and not traumatizing.

CHAPTER 22

Kingman Boys and Girls Club

I look back on the many wonderful and stress-free summer camp days I had at Kingman Boys and Girls Club with glee. My Uncle Cliff was the program director. Aside from my grandparents, he was my saving grace. At 6'7", he joined Kingman Boys and Girls Club in the early 1970s, after a brief stint at Tennessee State College, where he played basketball on a scholarship. Kingman was a special place started by a group of residents to shield neighborhood children from the chaos in our Shaw/Logan Circle community, which was then a blighted neighborhood.

The late John Thomas Sr, a Hall of Fame coach at Georgetown University, was one of the founding members. Dick Peters, a white man and local businessowner, donated an old tire warehouse in an alley that was used as an educational and recreational center for youth. Mr. Peters was actively involved in planning and growing the organization for many years. He often visited the club, on Christmas he dressed as Santa Claus, and brought gifts to the annual parties. He was a nice and charitable man.

Kingman was full of kids year-round. It sheltered us from the mayhem. My uncle's leadership changed the trajectory of hundreds of children's lives. His support, guidance, and love gave a lot of young people hope and an opportunity to erase the achievement gap between poor Black kids and their more affluent white peers who lived in a different zip code.

Many of the student-athletes who played on Kingman's sports teams, mainly football and basketball, earned scholarships to play at the collegiate level.

The counselors were older youth and young adults from the neighborhood. They had good relational trust. They were loving, caring, and modeled good character. In the summers, we met on the basketball court first thing in the morning for roll call, stretched and exercised, and got our counselor assignments.

We had a game room with a pool table, ping pong table, arts and crafts room, photography, and a library. In the summer, we went on field trips to the various museums, swam, and played in various basketball, football, and baseball tournaments. We participated in neighborhood cleanup campaigns to remove graffiti and trash. I remember painting the fire hydrants to look like community workers.

Once there was canoe excursion along the Potomac River that was featured in the local newspaper. Outside, adjacent to the building, jammed into a small patch of land between two converging alleys, we had a makeshift basketball court with a single rim. We loved that court and had some fierce games and competitions.

But one summer night when I was 11 years old, I nearly died on that court. My childhood best friend Kermit and I snuck into the Kingman building after hours, being mischievous. An employee, an older man name Jimmy who ran the print shop, was working late. We were running around, hollering, and acting silly. He saw us.

We went to the second floor, hung out of the windows, and dropped to the ground. I ran to the basketball court where two older teenagers were playing one-on-one. I sat on a plastic milk crate and tried to play it off like I had been there watching them.

Jimmy the left building and walked calmly toward me. He had a blank stare, psychotic-like. He walked closer, then he unexpectedly violently grabbed me by the neck with both hands and nearly choked me to death. He was possessed. I could not get loose. He was too strong. I almost passed out.

Jake and John, the two teenagers who were playing basketball, rushed over and pried his hands from around my neck. He tried to kill me. Disoriented, gasping for air, I fell to the ground. Then I jumped up like a wounded animal and ran home. They saved me. A week later, Jimmy was shot dead across the street from my house. He tried to stop a man from confronting a prostitute across the street from my house. He died with his eyes wide open. Karma.

We later learned that Jimmy was not his real name and that he was living under an alias. And that he had killed before. A few years later, Jake (my hero) committed suicide over his girlfriend cheating on him. He was in his late twenties. I was traumatized by these experiences, and they exacerbated my anxiety and fear. Back in those days, there was no therapy for these tragic experiences, whether you were a child or adult, when bad things like this happened. You suppressed your feelings and survived the best way you could. But it came with a cost.

PART 2

CHAPTER 23

The Stressful
Teenage Years

The teenage years are a period of tremendous change. We began to separate ourselves from our parents, identify more with our peers, and we take more risks. As the brain restructures itself toward adulthood, we are susceptible to make mental and emotional errors in judgement and decision making. And when we have trauma histories, we flounder emotionally in life, unable to get our mental equilibrium.

Our brains are more susceptible to stress during this period. The executive functioning part of our brains does not fully mature until our mid-twenties. It is in the front of our brains, behind our foreheads. This part of the brain is responsible for decision making, forethought, planning, impulse control, judgement, and social engagement. Basically, it controls how we react and respond to life's challenges in a responsible way.

As I grew up and adapted, my mind-body was trying to catch up with the anxieties of being a teenager. My sensitive personality, high stress reactivity, and lack of coping skills made the teenage years a challenge.

In junior high school, I struggled academically. I did not like school. This was a stressful time for me. I was a loner. My grades were bad, and I ditched class. I realize now I could not focus on school because of the stressful events taking place in my neighborhood.

My amygdala (emotional brain) and vagus nerve were over aroused by the environmental threats of unsafety and violence. The vagus nerve sends and receives chemical and electrical messengers between our brain and body, stimulating many organs associated with the fight or flight or freeze system. Children living in violent and crime-ridden neighborhoods, like me, are prone to be hypervigilant. On guard mentality waiting for the next shoe to drop. Their higher-order thinking brain, called the neocortex (executive functioning), is shut down by the more immediate mind's concern: survival.

One day, me and Kermit played hooky from school and went fishing at a nearby creek. A strange man propositioned us for sex. We threw rocks at him and ran up a hill on to a street. The police picked us up. They asked, why we were not in school? We tried to change the subject and told them about the man. They walked us back to the creek, and the guy was still there. He denied ever seeing us. The police returned us to school.

My Uncle Cliff feared where I was headed and transferred me to another junior high school, where he had a friend who coached basketball. I did not care much about playing basketball, nor doing any schoolwork, but my uncle encouraged me to do it. In retrospect, I was not dumb. He asked Eddie Myers and Jay Shorter, two well-respected basketball coaches, to mentor me. Coach Myers would pick me up from home, take me to practice, and serve as a positive role model. He took me to my first basketball camp at Rutgers University and bought me some sneakers. I was amazed by the size of the place. It had a lot of basketball courts, and it was clean.

There were lots of white kids, people I never interacted with where I came from. One of my teammates had an argument with one of them. He asked the boy to come in the bathroom to fight. Then he removed dirt out of a flowerpot, put it in his hands, and balled up his fist. The boy declined.

The Stressful Teenage Years

We learned at basketball camp social skills and how to get along with kids from different racial backgrounds. The counselors mixed up the campers, putting Black and white kids on the same teams. Before the camp ended, I had made some new friends from a different race.

At Langley Jr. High School, Jay Shorter was my basketball coach. He was an awesome coach and mentor. He often called me on the phone and checked on me on a regular basis. He helped a lot of Black kids from tough parts of the city get to the next level in high school. I was tall for my age. At 14, I was 6'4" and wore a size 14 shoe. Playing sports boosted my self-esteem and kept me out of trouble. My baseline personality was quiet and self-doubting.

Kermit and I went our different ways at this age. I traveled a different path playing sports. I was featured in a newspaper article titled, "They're dunking in Jr High." I spent more time practicing basketball and less time hanging out with my neighborhood friends who I often got into trouble with doing stupid and illegal stuff. I even joined a church for a brief stint and was baptized. During this period, I worried about dying. I do not remember what prompted this existential rumination, but I was preoccupied with it. Maybe it was a culmination of the neighborhood turmoil colliding with my teenage emotions.

Those years are times of major psychological and emotional uncertainty and insecurity. I was trying to find myself, always thinking and questioning what my purpose on this planet was. I didn't fit in with the crowd. One day, I was at a friend's house; his mother was a devout Christian. I heard some strange noise coming from their living room. I was curious and drawn to the mysterious sound. I asked my friend, "what is the noise?

He replied, "My mother is praying. She is speaking in tongues."
"What does that mean?" I asked.
"She has the spirit of God, the holy ghost."
I asked him, can I talk to your mother when she has done

praying? "Sure."

As she knelt on the floor, I asked her, "can you pray for me?". She smiled, reached out her hands and grabbed mine I knelt with her, closed my eyes and she prayed for me. I felt stress free after praying with her. She started taking me with her to church on Sundays, I was baptized. Some of the kids in the neighborhood started calling me names like Holy Roller, a derogatory term referring to devout religious people who shout and fling their arms in the air. I didn't do any of that, but I did carry my bible with me. I went to Sunday school and stayed out of trouble. I stopped worrying about dying because if I did, I knew I was going to heaven.

My anxiety and fears waned. As time went by, I stopped going to church but continued to believe. By this time, the neighborhood was starting to change, and so was I.

The 80s was an era of great social turmoil in many Black communities across the country tied to the introduction of a potent new street drug. By outward appearances, I had grown taller and gained some confidence as an elite youth basketball player. But on the inside, I harbored an inner nervousness that was always with me.

CHAPTER 24

Coach Williams:
Peaks and Valleys

Sometimes in life we all could use a good coach. I was recruited by many high school coaches. I was surprised one day when a well-known high school basketball coach drove to my house. He tried to sell me on why his school, which had a top team at the time, would be a suitable fit for me. I was not interested because the school was in the hood. I was trying to get out of the hood. I needed a better education and less stressful environment.

My Uncle Cliff tried to enroll me in Gonzaga an elite private school in Washington, DC. He drove me to the school, and I met the head coach. I was excited because the school had better resources than my neighborhood schools did at the time. They had better everything. Better textbooks, a well-kept building, gardens, cafeteria with great food, regulation size indoor basketball courts, and a football field. The students wore suit jackets and neck ties. I was impressed but intimidated at the same time. I failed the private school exam. They did not admit me. I was bummed.

My uncle called a friend and basketball coach at Coolidge High School in another part of the city, far away from where I lived. Frank Williams was a former basketball star at Howard University. He was dedicated to helping youth, particularly disadvantaged ones. He knew the power of building relational trust with kids. I liked Coach Williams right away.

He was soft spoken, like my grandfather. He was kind and honest, someone who I could relate to and trust. He often picked me up from home to practice with him. That made me feel special.

He took me to 5 Star Basketball camp in Honesdale, Pennsylvania in his small sports car one summer. I still remember stuffing my 6'5" frame into his tight front seat. It was founded by the late great Howard Garfinkel. Back in the day, the elite basketball players went there, and college coaches flocked in groves to see and evaluate the best athletes in the country. The camp was expensive, at least for my family. Coach Williams was one of the coaches on staff. Since I could not afford the camp, he arranged for me to clean tables along with other campers to offset the fee.

The recognition I received from playing basketball, coupled with Coach Williams' mentorship, improved my self-esteem. He was a father figure and often counseled me through many emotional challenges. I remember the first time I appeared in the local newspaper selected as an All-Metropolitan basketball player my grandparents were so proud of me.

I was most comfortable and relaxed on the court, very tough and aggressive. I had a habit of throwing elbows which is forbidden in basketball. At 16, I was punched in the face by a 30-year-old, muscular man for elbowing him on the neighborhood court playing pickup. I didn't cry, though.

Shy by nature, I kept to myself. I only allowed a few people to get to know me. I struggled emotionally as a teenager and nearly flunked out of high school.

Coach Williams cared about me and other athletes; he dedicated his life to helping youth. He spent many years before his untimely death coaching young boys about more than the X's and O's on the basketball court. He taught his athletes about the virtues of life.

Coach Williams: Peaks and Valleys

Often, I came to school upset or sad. I struggled during those teenage years with low self-esteem. In reflection, I cherish the time Coach Williams spent helping me. He stayed on me about keeping my grades up. He talked teachers when I failed classes and asked them to give me another chance. I barely graduated with a C average.

I remember one day I was having one of my mad, dysregulated moments, when he stopped me in the hallway and asked, "what's wrong today, Darryl?" I rambled on about problems with my girlfriend and stress related to neighborhood issues.

He put his hand on my shoulder, looked me in the eye, and said, "Darryl, you have to get rid of these peaks and valleys in your life. One day you are happy and the next day you are sad. They are interfering with your academic and emotional growth." I believe I suffered from anxiety and depression and did not know it. I did not go to social events with lots of people, such as parties, football games, or other sporting events held at my school to any other large social gathering for that matter. Typical social anxiety disorder symptoms.

I hope this story helps some young people in high school feeling the way I did, like an outcast not knowing why they are different. Nowadays, people with a range of developmental and cognitive and emotional and behavioral differences are being more widely accepted not as abnormal but neurologically diverse. Accept yourself as unique and special, not flawed. It will lessen the stress of being viewed as different. You don't have to fit in; just be yourself.

CHAPTER 25

Mentoring

Mentors are a great source of buffering. I met my mentors, Kent Amos, and Jane Rand, while in high school in the 1980s. They both worked for the Xerox corporation at the time. Kent Amos was a native Washingtonian and former Calvin Coolidge High School student and graduate of Delaware State University. He had done well for himself at Xerox and achieved the American dream as a successful Black businessman.

Jane Rand was from Detroit, Michigan. She had become a success at Xerox as well. They both got involved in the Washington, DC community mentoring boys and girls. Jane had seen the devastation in her hometown of Detroit when the automobile industry closed. Other businesses soon followed, and a once-thriving hub of America's economic might had fallen to its knees. Detroit's financial hardships caused unemployment rates to soar, along with crime and mental health and other health disparities. Similar socioeconomic disparities were evident in America's major urban cities, particularly in Black and brown communities, like Washington, DC at that time. She and Kent Amos made a difference.

Kent Amos' children, Wesley, and Debbie, enrolled at Coolidge. Wesley played with me on the basketball team. My first memory of Mr. Amos was after we had won a summer league tournament, the team went to Shakey's Pizza, and we celebrated. He bought the food. He was articulate, successful, and lived in a wealthy area not far from the school.

Mentoring

I admired his success.

On a bus trip to a game one day, he gave me a copy of the book, *Think and Grow Rich* by Napoleon Hill. Back then I was not into school that much. But the book's title piqued my interest. What poor Black person would not want to know how to Think and be Rich?

I read different passages from the book from time to time. I was not ready socially and emotionally to put its success principles into practice, but they both mentored me.

I was a curious teenager, but self-doubting. Mr. Amos was a handsome man, successful and well connected with some of the most important people in society. Mrs. Rand was well read, intelligent, and my mother figure. We had a mutual connection of kindness, friendship, and I admired the genuine interest she took in me.

She turned me on to books and sparked my natural curiosity to learn, a trait I had always but had yet to discover. She shared many books with me over the years. She and I share a love for reading nonfiction books, particularly self-help titles.

We formed a mentoring relationship that has lasted for more than 40 years. They both were there for me through some tough times, such as when my grandparents died, my breakups, when I got into trouble and through my mental health challenges, and job stresses. They have been a dedicated friends, buffers, and mentors. Ms. Rand told me to read *Emotional Intelligence* by Daniel Goleman when it was published in 1995. I liked that book a lot. It gave me some great advice on how to model social and emotional learning skills with my children.

I used bibliotherapy, the process of reading and gaining insight and knowledge to work through my issues. I acquired vital information that helped me understand myself, stress impact on me, and ways to manage it more successfully. I like bibliotherapy because I can be selective about the type of information I choose to read. I am a non-fiction person. I like learning things I can apply to my everyday life that is factual and based on science. I love reading about real people who overcame insurmountable problems to achieve success. Most of the books I read focused on mental health and brain science.

My daughters have told me everybody is not interested in that stuff, Dad. I get it, but nor was I many years ago. Then I was exposed to information about important subjects that I related to that opened my eyes. I did not read when I was younger, but I began to realize how much smarter and self-aware I had become with each book I read. The point of this story is having someone in your life who cares for you, gives you constructive and meaningful guidance, and equally important gives you a different perspective about life is crucial to managing stress and problem solving. Both these people encouraged me to read. The books I read improved my mental health in so many ways.

I never gave up my will to get my life back and bibliotherapy helped with that. I went to various bookstores and searched for books that caught my eye. It was an interesting time because I was still in the throes of anxiety disorder and was constantly having panic attacks. Standing in a busy public bookstore around other people was the last place I wanted to be.

The urge to leave those uncomfortable feelings made me want to escape, but I knew to extinguish that fear I had to confront my fear. It's what Joseph Wolpe, the famous psychologist, called desensitization. And it was knowledge like that I learned from bibliotherapy. Before I knew it, I had dozens of titles on various subjects in my library. Applied information truly is power. Often, I would skim through the book at first to get a feel for the information, to see if I liked how the author was delivering their message. I instantly liked some books right away. Sometimes the titles were misleading.

I read lots of books on anxiety and depression. I learned about the causes of anxiety and depression. The best treatments available at the time. I learned that I was not going crazy and that in time I would get my life back. I constantly connected the dots in my life and put them together, and it made sense to me. Soon my mind accepted my new belief and attitude that what I was feeling was temporary. Each insight gleaned from another source was therapy.

I often call my mentor Jane and we talk a lot about the books and why I liked them. Having her to talk to in conjunction with reading the books was therapeutic as well. Especially because she was so empathic and concerned about me. She knew I was in search of information and growing as a person. She sent me more information in the form of newspaper and magazine articles on various mental health topics that helped me a lot.

The internet has made bibliotherapy an attractive way to get information. I would not recommend self-diagnosing yourself. Unless you are a trained mental health professional, you might misinterpret something. Making that mistake may cause you harm and even more stress and mental problems.

CHAPTER 26

College Stress

I attended George Washington University (GWU) on a basketball scholarship. I was an exceptional high school basketball player who was recruited by some big-time schools: The University of Connecticut, Georgia Tech, Clemson University, the University of Pittsburgh, Boston University, and the University of Maryland, to name a few.

My college coach had to convince the college admission officers to accept me because my grades were bad, and my SATs were terrible. On my high school transcript, I had some D's, some F's, a lot of C's, and at the bottom in the right-hand corner a handwritten comment by the counselor read, "He's an exceptional athlete with a pleasing personality, but needs help with remedial math and reading." I entered college lagging far behind the other students academically. And mentally I was at a disadvantage too. None of that demonstrated my potential to succeed in college.

On paper it may have appeared I was incapable of succeeding in college, but my innate intelligence was dormant. My grandparents did not go to college. They were unaware of how to guide me academically, but socially and emotionally, they had given me a solid foundation. The tough neighborhood I came from was different and had imprinted me with a scattered mind.

As a freshman, I had no clue how to navigate the predominantly white college atmosphere that was foreign to me. I felt nervous and out-of-place most of the time but hid it. My anxiety-stricken personality made it hard for me to participate in classroom discussions, even if I thought I had an answer I kept quiet.

I struggled in the classroom and on the court for two different reasons, both related to my stress reactivity and anxious personality. My college coach was nothing like my grandfather and high school coach. He caused me a lot of stress because of his demanding and hypercritical coaching style. He knew how talented I was and what my potential could be, but his attempt to motivate me backfired. Instead of getting the best out of me, he stressed me out, and I shut down.

The pressure was on me and other top-rated freshmen to contribute right away to the team. Our coach was a demanding, old-school guy. His approach to motivate his players was like a drill Sargent in boot camp. My freshman class, we had three Black players and three white players join the team. None of us knew one another when we started. By race, both groups gravitated toward each other. During a pregame meal at a hotel, the white players sat at one table and the Black players sat together; it was a scene right of a movie. We did not notice it.

Our coach entered the room, saw it, and went off. He said, "What is this? We have the whites sitting over and the Blacks sitting here." Then he stormed out of the room. He did not handle it well, but his message was clear: how could we be unified team we were divided by race? The captains on the team responded by having some of the whites and Blacks sit together. It was stressful at first having to sit and talk with someone who you did not have a lot in common with at first. However, I learned we had more in common than we realized. These expectations put pressure on coaches who then pass the pressure down to their players.

I was stressed out. I tried to quit. One day I refused to go to practice; I was crying, depressed. My coach came by and encouraged me to hang in there. One practice the coach was riding me badly, I literally ran out of practice and went home. I had had enough. The coach came to my house and convinced me to return. I did, but the stress continued. The coach got on me more than any other players on the team. His approach to motivate me did not work. I was sensitive, not in a weak way but personality wise as it related to temperament. His tactics were to get the most out of his athletes, but the strategy didn't work with me. Fortunately for me, George Washington University's athletic department had committed people on staff to help student-athletes be successful. Sheila Hoban was my academic advisor, and Ellen Carter Woodbridge was an academic tutor. They monitored my academic progress when needed, but more importantly, they buffered me as much as they could from the stressful demands of being a Division One student-athlete.

Ellen Carter Woodbridge is a wonderful person. She was my English teacher my freshman year. Her kind spirit, pleasant smile, and giving heart reminded me of my grandparents. She was a buffer for me at GWU. She often treated me to meals at Bob's Big Boy when we studied. I was conditioned in the Pavlovian way. As time passed, she would offer me to dinner, and I would excitedly (unconsciously) grab my books and study material. She invited players on the team to her wedding. There I had my first taste of caviar.

During my sophomore year, I had just left my Criminal Justice class, headed to my next class, when I heard a whimpering female on the phone. Her voice sounded panicky and terribly upset. Curious, I broke my stride to make out what the sadness was about. My interest was more out of concern than nosiness. She was hysterical because she had gotten a poor grade on an exam. I assumed she failed to meet her mark. College is a stressful time for many students.

Many people experience their first symptoms of depression during their college years. Unfortunately, many college students who have depression are not getting the help they need. They might not know where to go for help, or they believe treatment will not benefit them. Others do not get help because they think their symptoms are just part of the typical stress of college, or they worry about being judged if they seek mental health care. Being a freshman away from home for the first time can be an overwhelming experience. And each year after that has its share of responsibilities and demands that can keep the stress wheel turning.

I had another mentor, Thomas V. Hicks, an older Black man from Chicago. He was one of my tutors. He was a prolific writer. He insisted that I read and read some more. In fact, he was adamant I read. He said it would broaden my worldview and that it would improve my writing. He said, when you read, watch how the writers write, their style of writing, pay attention to the cadence in their writing, and soon you will catch on and find yourself writing better. He helped to ease my stress about writing and increased my confidence.

During the summer break, I was working on a genealogy project. I was motivated by Ann Webster, no relation, an Anthropology teacher whose class I had taken. I was fascinated and interested in learning about my family tree, who my ancestors were. I was curious about their trials and adversities they endured, and the role stress played in their lives. I went to one of the oldest known living relatives in my family at the time. Aline Wilson, lived on my street just a few houses down. She and her husband were in their 80s.

They lived alone in their own row house. Both were restricted to the bed by age and health infirmities. I revered the elderly. Being raised by my grandparents influenced my love and admiration for them. Visiting my uncle and aunt was sad. They were lonely. I witnessed firsthand the impact of being alone and the power of being together. My presence perked them up.

During my visits, I would shave my uncle. He had a long gray beard and whiskers that had grown wild and woolly. As I lathered on the shaving crème and massaged it into his beard, he closed his eyes and purred like a cat. After being alone for so long, they enjoyed the human contact, especially the joy of human touch. Then, I cut both of their toenails, which had grown out a great deal. Afterwards, I proceeded to interview my aunt. She was a strong and fierce entrepreneur in her heyday, my grandmother had told me. She had owned a few properties.

I received a special history lesson from her unlike anything I had been exposed to in school. I had a living witness to history in front of me. She laid in bed, her voice booming with remembrance, her stories rich in family lore. Harrowing tales of my great-great-grandmother, a Cherokee Indian, who lived during the Civil War. She had lived to be 105 years old. President Eisenhower sent her a congratulatory letter on her 100 birthdays. I was moved on one occasion to share with her my stress at college and the coach. I told her how much I was stressed out with everything.

She leaned up slightly from a lying position, turned her head toward me, and spoke in a deep voice. "Don't let nobody or anything make you quit. The next time you're confronted with any adversity at college, remember these words, "plead my cause Lord with thee, fight against those that fight against me." She added, "that will give you strength." Her words gave me the confidence to not quit. It was a mantra that empowered me the rest of my college days. It worked.

CHAPTER 27

Stress Management Class

In my sophomore year in college, I needed an elective course. Since stress is a part of my life, I enrolled in a Stress Management class. I was drawn to the class because I was frustrated, juggling academics, and playing basketball. There was a lot of pressure to do well in both. Being on scholarship has its perks, but it's demanding. When big time college sports programs or any college sports program give you thousands of dollars in the form of paying for your housing and your classes, textbooks, and food, they want something in return. They want a commitment that you will devote your time to be the best student athlete you can be. And that is a fair tradeoff with one exception: we must understand the stress factor.

Back then, stress wasn't a part of the conversation when discussing student-athletic performance and the demands made on young people and their impact on them mentally. We know more today about the correlation between stress and mental illness, especially on college campuses and the pressures on student athletes. Intuitively, I knew stress was a major part of my undoing. I noticed a Stress Management class in the course guide, I was motivated. I signed up.

The class was in a nondescript building on campus near the busy subway station. It was scheduled at 5pm, which is around rush hour in Washington DC. During this time campus was buzzing with activity of students coming from and going to class, government workers getting off work headed to the subway and traveling by car. There was tons of foot and vehicle traffic on the street as well. It was interesting, watching everyone on the move in the doing mode.

The class made me aware of how detached we are from ourselves; we go about our daily routine like robots programmed to do the same things day and day out with little conscious awareness. Honey was the professor. She was an elegant lady, the perfect person to teach this class. Her demeanor and presence were calm, positive, and friendly. For me, some professors were intimidating to approach. Not Professor Nashman. I was excited to be in her class and her style of teaching made the class fun and motivated me to study hard.

In some classes I was reluctant to speak up. My temperament was reserved, self-doubting, nervous, and afraid to answer questions for fear I would be wrong, and people would think critically of me. I thought my questions were stupid, or that I was not as articulate as the other students. Insecurities related to implicit childhood memories.

Things were different for me in this class. I felt a sense of agency. The subject matter was of great interest to me. I could not stop reading them. I learned about Hans Selye, the Czech Canadian scientist known as the father of the stress movement and Walter Cannon, a Harvard researcher who discovered the fight-or-flight response. I learned about the connection between thoughts (real or imagined) particularly threatening, fear-provoking ones and how they trigger the stress response.

I learned how stress affects the human body and brain. For me, it was interesting and informative at the same time. I was able to connect my personality, social stressors, and upbringing to my anxiety and changes in mood. I learned some basic knowledge of how the human brain and body worked together through billions of nerve cells communicating back and forth between the brain and other organs in the body. I was captivated by the information and the wonderful women who taught it. I got insights about myself that I never had considered.

One was how the mind and body stress connection is inseparable and how our perceptions of things can trigger the stress response. I read a lot trying to grasp the concepts related to stress physiology. I found the class fascinating, because I had found a logical scientific reason for my behaviors and strategies to rewire my brain.

First, I learned about Triune Brain, a theory of Paul D. Maclean. He says the brain evolved and developed over time from a very primitive to more advanced and sophisticated brain with three distinct parts: the Reptilian Brain, aka lizard brain; the limbic system, known as the emotional brain; and the newest part, the Neocortex, aka the prefrontal cortex. It is in the front of our skulls, behind our foreheads. It is also called the executive function because it controls most of our higher order thinking abilities, such as impulse control, judgement, decision making, planning, and social skills. It does not fully develop until around the age of 25 years or so.

For my class assignment, I chose Walter Cannon. Though experimentation with animals, he identified the physiological changes occur when living creatures, particularly mammals, are under threat, real or imagined. He called it the fight, flight, or freeze response. I laughed to myself when I read about his experiments with lab rats. I had had my own real-life lab experienced in my own home.

Our nervous system is highly reactive to negative thoughts of any kind, our minds do not differentiate between real or perceived threats, the body/mind responds physiologically as if the actual event or thing has happened. For example, if you perceived yourself getting evicted and visualized your belongings sitting on the street and you and your family had no place to go, just the thoughts alone could raise your blood pressure. Cortisol plays a lot of roles in regulating organ functioning. But in this case, it gets the ball rolling by preparing the body to fight/flight/freeze. Cortisol affects the circulatory system by diverting blood to large muscles to run or fight, it temporally suspends the immune function, it causes the release of glucose for energy, the heart rate to increase, the eyes to dilate to help us see better, and for adrenaline to rev up the body.

For my classroom project, I gave the students a stress card that was the size of a credit card. It had small multicolored legend that illustrated the amount of tension felt that corresponded with a color. A red square for tense, a blue for relaxed, green for calm, and black for stressed. And a small square spot in the middle to place your finger. You pressed your finger on the spot and it gave you a reading, a color indicating your stress level.

The spot was temperature sensitive. When we are stressed, one of the ways the body prepares for threats is by diverting blood away from some body parts, including the fingers, and sending it to larger ones to fight off the predator or run away. When this happens, our hands (fingers) turn cold because there is less blood flow. Have you ever had someone shake your hands and say, "your hands are cold"? You probably were under some stress that day unless you have an underlying health condition.

Based on how cold or warm your fingers where the square would show a color to indicate that. The students used the cards and to their surprise there were color differences indicating their stress level. Some people were really stressed, and others were calm. It was an easy way to demonstrate the stress response. They loved it and got to keep the stress cards too.

CHAPTER 28

Blindsided by Life

In the spring of 1987, I had just graduated from George Washington University (GWU). I was 23 years old. I was not sure what to do with my life. My adulthood started in the most traumatic way. My girlfriend of six years left me for another guy, and I lost my high school basketball coach, Frank Williams and then an uncle. I thought things were bad, but it got worse.

My grandparents died two months apart in the most unexpected way. That May, an elderly neighbor in her 90s, Ms. Jones, had locked herself out of her house. My 72-year-old grandfather tried to enter the first-floor window of her four- story row house to retrieve her keys. He fell and broke his leg. I ran down to Ms. Jones' house and saw him crumpled up on the ground with his leg grotesquely twisted back under his body. I tried to console him. He quietly, with disappointment uttered under his breath, "That was stupid."

I responded, "No it wasn't, you were just trying to help her." I thought it was a kind and thoughtful thing for him to do.

After several weeks in the hospital, he was sent home with screws inserted and his leg in a cast. Then, late one night, my grandmother called me to come quick. Something was wrong with him. I rushed to his room where he sat in a chair with his arms folded across his chest, rocking back and forth, grimacing in great pain. I reached out to touch him.

He shouted, "No, call the ambulance!" Two ambulances arrived.

Paramedics put him in one and I followed in the other. On the way to the hospital, I noticed the siren of his ambulance sound changed. I asked my driver, why? He responded, "He's in cardiac arrest." My heart dropped. Both vehicles arrived at the emergency door at the same time. I jumped out and ran over as they pulled him out on the gurney. One paramedic walked alongside of him, pumping aggressively on his chest. He pushed him into the emergency room.

My Uncle Clifford and I and other family members paced the floor, worried, and stressed. After a couple hours, the doctors came out and said, "I'm sorry your loved one expired." A blood clot had moved from the broken leg and traveled to his heart. That was the saddest day of my life. My beloved grandfather and father figure was gone. My uncle and I cried; we hugged each other and went back home to tell my grandmother the tragic news. She lay in bed, not expecting it. My Aunt Constance knelt beside her bed and in a quiet voice told my grandmother that her husband of nearly sixty years, was dead.

Her facial expression was lifeless, grief stricken. She teared up. And responded, in a whispery, sad voice, "You're kidding." My grandfather's death was a shock to everybody. Although he was 72-years old, he was a healthy and strong man who looked a decade younger. His funeral was a sad occasion. The patriarch and a beloved member of the community was gone. For me, it had an even more traumatic because it was my first funeral. At the wake, I laid my head on my mother's lap and cried the whole time. I will never forget the long processional of cars traveling to the graveyard. I looked out of the back window of the limousine. As far as I could see, there were cars with people coming to say goodbye.

So many people, why? He was not a sports star, or admired entertainer, revered political leader, or wealthy benefactor. He was a common man, with an exceptional gift of empathy and selflessness.

Maya Angelou said, "People won't remember what you say, they won't remember what you do, but they will always remember how you make them feel." I found solace knowing he died helping someone in need and that he had touched throngs of people's lives in simple but extraordinary ways. Two months later, my grandmother died from a broken heart. And my heart was broken as well.

My grandparents' deaths were a traumatic experience for me. When I returned home, Q Street was not the same. The room where my grandparents slept side by side in single beds was empty. Their presence no longer occupied this old house. Has there been a major life event that has triggered your anxiety and depression, that has delayed your goals in life, and that has made you question the meaning of life? We come to a crossroads at different times in our lives when we are met with difficult and emotional, even tragic events that test and challenge us. I used the memories and the values they instilled in me to go forward to live my best life.

CHAPTER 29

Divine Intervention

Like most 20-somethings, I was not sure what I was going to do with my life. My grandparents were gone. I needed a job. My mother lived in Waldorf, Maryland, a long way from where I lived in DC. I had a college degree. I thought it should not be a problem getting a job. But it was. I do not know where the idea to work as a manager at McDonalds came about, but it did.

When you are young and not clear on a career path, and still grieving the deaths of family members and friends, it is hard to focus. I feared the taunting from my friends working at McDonalds, so I thought I would work at one near my mother's house, far away, where none of my friends would see me.

The first day of my training was in February 1987. A nor'easter had dumped more than 14 inches of snow in the Washington, DC region the week before my start date. After the storm cleared, I woke up one cold morning at 5:30am, prepared to travel to Waldorf. I had a small bag with a change of clothes. It was early in morning and still dark outside.

The streets and roads were filled with snow. Walkways and driveways were impassable. But the main streets had been plowed. I owned a small Ford Escort at the time. I was broke. I drove south with three bald tires; the fourth one was a spare. I made it to a local park way and realized I was running late. I drove even faster, maybe 60 mph or so. I was young and dumb.

The parkway was divided by trees and in some spots, they were deep ditches and other forestry. As I came around a winding, twisting road curving to the right, I hit a patch of black ice and began to hydroplane. I had no control of the vehicle. I was shocked. My car was headed straight ahead off the road toward a bunch of big trees down in a gully.

Instinctively, I pressed on the breaks hard, to no avail, then turned the steering wheel aggressively to the right, away from the direction toward the trees. The speed and momentum at which I was traveling, with the abrupt turn of the steering wheel, forced the vehicle to turn and flip wildly to the right, away from the ditch.

The vehicle flipped over three or four times on its roof. I was disoriented but felt the violent force of the car roof slamming against the pavement as my car tumbled forcefully and wildly out of control. It felt like I was blindfolded on a roller coaster in a bumper car as the car flipped over and over and over. Then suddenly, surprisingly, my car landed softly. It was eerily quiet. I was cushioned by 5' foot snow pile on the other side of the road.

After my brain got its equilibrium back, I realized I was still in my car, upside down. It looked like I was in the clouds. My initial thought was I had died and gone to heaven. Then I realized I was still in the car and had landed in a huge pile of snow upside down. It had cushioned my landing.

I was not hurt, not even a scratch. I opened the door and fell out into the snow and thanked God. The wheels were still spinning. I grabbed my bag of clothes and started walking down the road. I glanced back at my car and shook my head. That was stupid; why was I driving at such a fast speed?

I was thankful to be alive. Then a woman pulled up beside me rolled down her window, she looked surprised. She said, "I saw the skid marks around the turn. Were you in that car?"

"Yes", I responded.

"Oh boy you are truly blessed. Can I drop you off at that the next turnoff so you can get help?"

"Yes, thank you."

My vehicle was a total loss.

That was a sign I was not supposed to be a McDonald's manager. God had another assignment for me. Not having any transportation made that job impossible. I believe it happened for a reason. I interviewed for a police job; I do not know why. I did not get it. Desperate, not long after that, I looked in the newspaper classified ad and saw a low paying counselor position working with neglected and abused children. The Boys and Girls Club of Greater Washington offered the job. It was a few blocks from my house, within walking distance. Perfect.

There were four kids living in the house. Each of them had their social histories of neglect. I thought it was a great idea to provide them with a surrogate family to take care of them. They reminded me of my upbringing and how my grandparents had helped others.

I could not help but think, my being there was divine intervention. I settled into the job and hit it off with the boys. It did not seem like a job. They were family. I saw a lot of myself in those kids. By this time, I had replaced my Escort with an old, dark green 1972 Dodge Plymouth an aunt gave me from my deceased uncle.

It was a classic car.

Only the driver's door worked, though. To get through the passenger door, you had to climb through the window. With one of my first few pay checks; I bought a leather briefcase. The purpose of it was to put my future books and other materials when I went to graduate school. I was claiming it.

By coincidence, on the day I bought it, my mother had visited the house. She noticed the briefcase. "You bought that?"

"Yes, it's for graduate school."

"Why would you buy a briefcase for college, and you don't know if you can get into it and you haven't applied yet?" she said.

I told her I was manifesting my dream, the law of attraction.

CHAPTER 30

Helping Kids Navigate
the Landfill of Dreams

My grandparents had told me regardless of how bad life gets, there is always someone worse off than you and helping them will make you feel better. One day, not long after I had started working at the group home, a lady named Dr. Lee, a college professor from Catholic University, brought some students there to tutor our residents. I was still grieving the deaths of my grandparents. I shared my story.

I expressed an interest in attending graduate school because my mentors said I would be more employable. She listened intently. Several weeks after our conversation. She called and told me the Catholic University of America (CUA) had a Fellowship in honor of Patricia Roberts Harris, a former cabinet member in President Carter's Administration, for Social Work for minorities. I asked her what exactly social workers do? She answered with a smile in her voice, doing what you are doing right now. I said, what is that? She added, helping people; from what I see, you are exceptional at it.

I rushed to the university to inquire about the fellowship. I met with the admissions person. He told me, young man there is a long waiting list for this award. But before you can be considered for it, you must apply to the school of social work. He gave me the admission packet. I rushed back to the group home and began filling it out.

I had just gone on the *Oprah Winfrey Show* with my mentor. I ask permission to allow one of the children from the group to travel with me. We had taken a picture with Oprah. Her show was just a year old at that point. I put that picture and the news article in the admission packet and returned it. I only had a C average as an undergrad, so the chances of admission were slim. But I had faith, I knew my grandparents were watching over me. It was no accident that I ended up at this job. I called the admissions person every day checking on the admissions process.

Then a week later, he said, "You sure are persistent."

I responded, "I really want this."

He said, "Well good news you've been admitted to the school, but we have to wait on the Dean of Social Work to give the final answer."

I said, "Final answer for what?"

He responded, "There are three fellowships. Your name was given with two others for it, but the dean has the final say."

I jumped out of my seat with joy. I said that means I have it then. The dean later approved it. It was divine intervention, my calling. I laughed to myself when I put my books in my briefcase at that start of graduate school. I had manifested my dream.

To cope with losing my grandparents and to honor their legacy of giving back, I started a nonprofit organization in my community called the Youth Entrepreneurial Services (YES) in 1987. In fact, "YES" was the motto that we lived by, knowing that things are possible.

Our logo of a silhouette of a youth reaching up to the sky as the sun rose behind them symbolized a triumphant person who succeeded despite the adversities in life. My organization was established at a time when Washington, DC, was known as the murder capital of the nation. Black youths killed each other in record numbers as the crack epidemic lured many hopeless teens into a criminal world of making a quick dollar.

Local and national media covered my story, from articles in the *Washington Post* to being selected as a national hero and put on the cover of *USA Today*. My efforts to help children and youth were being recognized.

We should have hopes and dreams, but that is not the case for some people. I have had youth tell me they did not expect to live long enough to grow up, to finish high school or have a family. They viewed life from a fatalistic mindset. Their lives had been filled with disappointment, rejection, and trauma.

But despite their plight, some of these children demonstrated remarkable resilience. The YES program taught them the value of hard work, entrepreneurship, and the power of positive thinking. One of YES's primary functions was locating and obtaining odd jobs for youth. I designed a curriculum around a set of values and lessons I learned with the main goal of redirecting youth and teaching them the meaning of living a purposeful life. The program was a positive approach to helping youth earn money and stay out of trouble.

One memorable day stands out in my mind. I transported several children on a trash-hauling job. We traveled twenty miles outside of DC to a huge landfill covering dozens of acres of country land, as far as the eye could see. As we came along narrow, winding dirt roads, the youth talked excitedly about their goals and aspirations.

One of the youngsters named Larry, who had been neglected and abused since birth and who, with his siblings, was consistently left home alone for days on end with little food, was removed from his mother. Despite his horrible past, Larry possessed a positive view of the world. He said, "One day I'm going to own a clothing business." Another child named Jason said, "I am going to own my own sneaker business." I was inspired by their positive dreams and goals from kids who had major hurdles in their paths. Their positive expectations and vision were inspiring. As we came around a turn, there it was: the biggest depository of junk I have ever seen.

We watched people unload cars and trucks of their personal

items. Some things appeared never to have been used! Acres of barren land were the last resting place for discarded objects. I thought, "How many people have let their dreams and goals go into the landfill of broken dreams, a place where so many unrealized hopes for the future have disappeared, been discarded like junk, covered up beneath fear, stress, trauma, or guilt never to be used?" The landfill of dreams became the perfect metaphor. Do not let your dreams get covered up and forgotten about. It's never too late to live your dreams.

CHAPTER 31

Surviving a Public Health Crisis

Social scientists in early 1990s predicted the crack cocaine crisis in America would destroy a generation of Black children. The inner cities of America were overrun with a cheap street drug. In 1990, my son Christian was born. There was a *Washington Post* article dated January 2, 1991, titled "Washington Area's 703 homicides in 1990 set a record." I worried could I keep my son safe from the carnage on the streets.

I had already escaped my own environmental dangers a generation earlier. In his era, it was stress and violence on steroids; you could not take your kids outside to play. Innocent children and adults were killed in drive-bys. Being in the wrong place at the wrong time got you killed. Kids were being assaulted and robbed, even murdered for their sneakers.

My stress and anxiety levels were high. I had just taken my first job, as a social worker with the District of Columbia, Child and Family Services Administration (CSFA), which was under receivership. It was a low-paying, stressful job with a lot of risk, and to make matters worse to offset city financial deficits, I was furloughed one day per week. The crack cocaine epidemic was a public health crisis for urban families throughout the US. But no one was immune; violence found its way to more affluent neighborhoods.

Although I had grown a lot, the crack cocaine epidemic had

taken its toll on me. An outcry from many caused people to wonder why drugs and guns were being allowed into Black neighborhoods. Ironically, even though I was working, I still found myself living in a blighted but changing neighborhood.

I was determined, like my grandfather and his father before him, to help my child go further in life than I had done. I had the blueprint on how to successfully raise children and what not to do. I understood the impact of chronic stress on children's developing brains, so I knew I had to intentionally nurture my son in an attuned way to offset the reality that he could be killed on any day.

I tried hard to hide my fears and anxieties and not displace them on Christian like my mother had done inadvertently on me. I recognized that impressionable children are like sponges; they learn directly and vicariously from observing, from attunement and attachment. The emotions of their parents and family members are felt. I knew I had to smile and be responsive even when I was afraid. I did not want him to feel my anxiety and become anxious, too.

I saw the power of peer influence on the streets. Children whose parents did not form secure attachments lost them to their peers. As children get older, their peer groups have a stronger pull on them, and their parents lose their authority and emotional resonance. The emergence of 24-hour-a-day TV programming took the place of quality time with parents.

I preferred spending more of what the Harvard Department of Education calls serve and return time with my son, in other words playing and interacting with him, being attentive, and giving attunement that strengthened our bond. I modeled social and emotional learning skills. I knew he needed them to navigate life on the mean streets of DC and beyond in the broader society. I knew he could not get that from a TV screen or video game.

One day, a childhood friend, Terrance, saw me with my toddler son at a store. I held him affectionately in my arms and had his bottle sticking out of my back pocket. He looked surprised. Later, he told me one day at the gym. "I thought, what in hell is Darryl doing with a baby? He can't take care of that baby." His belief was based on erroneous perceptions of how we grew up, such as that Black men are not nurturers. Some people think men do not have the patience to care for babies or aren't sensitive enough to respond to infants in a loving way similarly to their mothers. Not true.

He did not know my potential as father and nurturer. I had the right stuff. I was sensitive, loving, and attuned, more so than my wife. Although we lived in the same neighborhood, each family was different. Some families were dysfunctional, and others were not. We were not a monolithic community.

We saw so many of our childhood friends get in trouble and stay in trouble; some just could not break free from the destructive imprint our neighborhood had on them. They became career criminals. Others had grown older without having done anything with their lives. It is no wonder he was shocked to see me with caring for my toddler son.

Obviously, some of us had changed more than others for the better or worse. Then I remembered this person had shared having a traumatic childhood with me.

Terrence told me, "when I was a child, 8 or 9, my father made me and my older brother fight each other until we bled, and if one of us cried, he'd beat us. He was trying to make us tough, instead he traumatized us, made me bitter and angry." He was projecting his traumatic childhood and misperception he had of me.

Over the years, I went to our local YMCA to play basketball with children. I saw the same friend on many occasions. One day, as he and I were talking, my daughter came over and grabbed my pants leg and pulled my arms; she was trying to get my attention to come play with her. I patiently responded to them. Give me a minute.

My friend looked puzzled. I asked him, what? He responded, "You're not stressed by her pulling and grabbing on you?

I responded, "No, it's not a big deal."

He added, "If that was my father, he would have slapped me across the room if I did that to him while he was talking to someone." I reminded him that as parents our children look to us how to respond and react to life situations, especially stressful ones and interpersonal relationships. It's important that we model appropriate social skills. We must help them co-regulate by staying in control of our emotions and behaviors. Over the years, I had learned to do that.

Obviously, his father had mistreated him and his brother, left awful painful memories with him, and failed to give him a childhood, he deserved: to be loved.

CHAPTER 32

Showing Up:
Be Present for your Child

Mentoring and parenting children came natural for me. The kindness and nurturing my grandparents had shown me with their empathetic concern and compassion was ingrained in my heart. My background in social work helped. My desire was to be with my son and longtime girlfriend. So, I stayed at her mother's apartment with them in the daytime. After I bathed Christian put him to bed, then I would walk home at night a few blocks away. I often heard gun shots or was solicited for sex by male prostitutes in the area. It became risky to walk home late at night. I decided to live there.

The apartment complex was in a heavy drug area at the time. There were shootings and some killings over neighborhood beefs, mostly teenagers and young adults. Although the neighborhood was changing, wholesale gentrification was still a couple decades away. I felt bad for the innocent people, the law-abiding people like myself, who went to work every day, and the senior citizens who had earned the right to live their remaining days peacefully. I had been familiar with tough neighborhoods growing up, but the level of violence during this era was unprecedented. When I was coming up, I could not recall adults using kids to sell drugs or be a part of violent criminal enterprises for that matter.

Poor Black kids, like any children, are impressionable. Poverty produces many intractable social problems. It destroys the human spirit. It made them vulnerable and easily swayed by the materialism to sell drugs. It was natural for them to want a better life. When your parents are too stressed to support and guide you properly, the peer group becomes surrogate parents. They offer acceptance and friendship. It was easy for their drug peddlers' peers to lure them into a culture of selling drugs. I was not going to let that happen to my son.

I could relate to the culture of poverty. The mindset that says do not try because you are not going to amount to anything, anyway. Nothing from nothing leaves nothing. When you are young and unaware and your brain is not fully developed, and perhaps toxic stress has left you anxiety stricken and depressed, you are vulnerable. They could buy clothes, help their parents pay bills, and impress others by driving fancy cars.

It was the summer of 1991, and a basketball tournament was in full swing across the street from the apartment complex. It was a hot but not uncomfortable, sunny day with a blue sky. The low-income units were built by the local Catholic Church in the 1960s. The residents were senior citizens, young single mothers, and families on fixed incomes.

On this day, sports fans gathered at the Kennedy Playground, named after the assassinated 35th President of the US, John F. Kennedy. The well-known playground in the heart of midtown DC was a popular site for basketball tournaments and other social events. Ironically, the playground named to honor a fallen hero would be defined by neighborhood violence.

On this day, my favorite sport was being played across the street from our window. At that moment, though, I was more interested in playing with my son. I had stopped watching and playing basketball years ago. I was depressed and had lost interest. However, the oohs and ahhs penetrating my window garnered my attention. I looked out the window and glanced toward the commotion. There was a crowd of people, young and old, standing watching the game. Side by side, they watched the game. Wide-eyed kids grabbed hold of the eight-foot-tall chain linked fence with excitement. The ballers were putting on a show. Everyone was having fun.

Mentally, I was in another world. My sense of detachment and flat affect coupled with dissociation was surreal. My love for my son, though, gave me the strength to continue living. I played with him. I flipped him over gently in his crib, trying not to hurt him. He smiled. Then he jumped up and down on his mattress like a trampoline. Within minutes, our happy moment was shattered by gunshots.

Instinctively, I grabbed and pulled him close to my chest on the floor. My heart was beating so fast. My chest pressed tightly against his small body; I could not hide my fear. I placed him down on the floor and crawled to the window, cracked the blends, and peeked out. The people had run away. As my eyes adjusted to the scene, I noticed an image laying on the ground.

Someone had been shot. Blood gushed from his head. A person was murdered. The gruesome sight depressed me. I felt sorry for the person who had lost their life. I picked Christian up and hugged him tightly. I worried if Christian, like many other children of this era raised in a violent neighborhood, would bear the psychological scars of trauma for years to come.

The police arrived.

I was shocked. People went back on the court and started shooting hoops again, and kids did the same with the dead body outside the fence. I was numb; my stress response was in overdrive.

I was determined that my son would not become another statistic or grow up anxious or depressed, like me, and even more alarming desensitize to the violence. Not another generation, no!!!!

We moved to Q Street.

CHAPTER 33

My twenties, a period of change

Transitioning from teenager to young adulthood came with a lot of change and stress for me. The days of being a teenager were over. For some people, the transition is not as difficult, because they are raised by parents or someone who prepared them for such an eventuality. For others, like me, it was a challenge. I found adulthood had its privileges, but it also represented a lot of stress and uncertainty, a time of great change and soul-searching.

My first bout with depression came after my first child was born, within months of my first job, at a time in my life when my role and responsibilities had changed. No longer was I living for myself. I had another life to care for and a demanding and stressful job. I could not escape the confining feelings that overwhelmed me. These changes required a level of maturity, confidence, and awareness I did not possess at the time.

My values to meet my parental responsibilities and job obligations overrode any fears I had. Being a father did not scare me. I love children and have a nurturing personality. My grandfather had nurtured and loved me; he showed me how to be a responsible man. I had his mindset, work ethic, and love for family and community.

It was the idea of going into the professional work world that intimidated me. Helping people came easy, but the daily grind of getting up reporting to a stressful job every day and being accountable in the way caused me a lot of stress. Beneath the surface, I struggled to cope mentally. A perfectionist, my goal was to raise my children to be social intelligent and to protect them from the evils in the world. When my son was a baby, I woke up during different times of the night and fed him and to change his diapers. I am a light sleeper, (part of my hyperarousal related to stress response) if he whimpered, I jumped up to check on him. I was responsive to his every need. When he cried, I picked him up right away. I had learned attunement meant responsiveness.

Prior to his birth, I went shopping at various stores looking for the right mattress and crib. I planned for my son to be as comfortable as possible. This ardent sense of parentage came from the love my grandfather had given me. It was not a chore for me; it was an act of love.

In the middle of the night if he cried, my wife nudged me and said the baby is crying. I felt such peace and a great sense of joy caring for my children, especially when they were infants; our brains are wired to respond to babies in that way.

My college education had given me knowledge of human and child development. I had read about rapid brain growth of infant during their first years of life. That knowledge was helpful. I was aware of the power of attunement. I was intentional. I hugged and kissed him every minute I could. I did not buy into the "I was spoiling him or making him weak" crap, it felt normal to love him in that way. I wanted him to know he was loved and that he was secure.

When he was a toddler, every time I was paid, we went to a toy store. The first toys I bought were not action figures they were sensory oriented.

Christian had a couple of friends in our neighborhood. Matthew was 5 years older than Christian. He was a foster child who lived with an elderly man on our street. I often picked Matthew up to come play with Christian. When I bought Christian a toy, I bought Matthew the same toy. I treated him like my son. I had learned that from my grandfather.

One winter evening, as the snow started to fall, people rushed home to hunker down. Christian asked to go to the Discovery Zone. It was a popular an indoor play area for kids back then. The attraction was a large maze that kids could run through and tumble. And there was an eatery.

I picked up Matthew. I knew about his background and always tried to involve him with positive events I shared with Christian. With heavy snow blanketing the area. I headed south out of the city to the suburbs with Christian and Matthew. We arrived and had the place to ourselves. I sat down at the eatery as the boys played nearby. They played and had a lot of fun. Afterwards, we sat down for pizza. I went up to the counter for more food. When I return to the table, Christian's eye was partially shut, and he was crying. I was shocked.

What happened I asked Christian? He nervously pointed at Matthew and said he hit me. It broke my heart. I hugged Christian and comforted him. Then I asked, Matthew, why did you hit him? He shrugged his shoulders and said, "I don't know." I hugged Matthew, then I said, "I'm disappointed that you would hurt Christian. It's not nice to hurt people, especially our friends. Give Christian a hug and tell him you are sorry." He looked puzzled.

Matthew had been neglected and abused; he had some challenges self-regulating and controlling his anger. I kept him with us as much as I could. In retrospect, I saw myself when I was his age, feeling envious toward my brother.

I surmised he was envious of Christian. Christian had everything he wanted, a doting Dad and a loving home. I continued to care for Matthew until he and Christian outgrew each other in their teenage years.

Matthew stopped coming by the house and started hanging with the wrong crowd. I heard in later years he was burned badly in a fire and later was murdered. It was so tragic, I told Christian. He was upset by the news. We both felt a great sense of loss.

If you have been exposed to toxic stress and trauma in your childhood, it could play an integral part in your inability to self-regulate, interfere with interpersonal relationships, disrupt your ability to work with others on a job, or be a loving and committed person in your marriage and other intimate relationships.

Self-awareness is the key to connecting the dots. And learning how to move pass being wounded many years ago. Each new day is a gift. An opportunity to grow to manifest your dream and celebrate life, to grow wiser, and take advantage of opportunities that await you.

CHAPTER 34

Where is Darryl?

Outside of my home, I was a no show. I did not go many places. Not because I was being uppity or selfish. My anxiety and depression symptoms were debilitating, life altering, downright miserable. It interfered with my ability to socialize and think rationally. I did not go to cookouts, birthday parties, weddings, sporting events, and regretfully missed a few of my children's sporting events in their earlier years.

Anxiety is a normal part of being human. It is a part of nervous system's way of alerting us there is something to prepare for that require our attention or a challenge to meet. When the everyday anxiety escalates to the extent, it disrupts our daily living in a major way, then it's classified as an anxiety disorder.

I had social anxiety disorder (SAD). I felt as if I were being judged and scrutinized by people. As if people were examining me from head to toe, finding flaws in how I looked, acted, or behaved. That belief and perception was a terrible burden to have. I felt ashamed of myself for no reason. My self-talk was negative and self-blaming, and a tsunami of worthlessness overwhelmed me. I refused to go anywhere for fear of being judged or ridiculed. With generalized anxiety disorder (GAD)—I had this condition too—it involved worrying about anything and everything with nothing to identify as a source of the worry.

The love for my children motivated me to overcome my mental illness. It was greater than my anxiety and depression. It forced me out of my discomfort zone, it gave me the strength to fight emotionally to be available for my children. I began spending more time practicing basketball with them, going to their games, and taking them on trips. I even went on an airplane and took Christian to a basketball camp when I hated to fly. I was not going to let anything get in the way of my giving my children a better life than I had.

I used systematic desensitization by going places despite having intense anxiety. I imagine myself successfully interacting with others in a relaxed state. I learned to used positive self-talk and reframed negative perceptions and viewing life's obstacles differently, having an optimistic mindset. If you have a habit of thinking negatively or catastrophizing, like I used to most likely, your anxiety is high. Our nervous systems do not differentiate between a real or imagined threat; they respond to what you tell it through your thinking, inner self-talk, and perception. My anxiety and depression would test my resilience in my first professional job as a social worker.

CHAPTER 35

Keeping Families Together

After I graduated from the Catholic University of America (CUA) in the fall of 1991, I left the group home and started my career as a front-line child protective services worker (CPS) in 1992, with the District of Columbia, Child and Family Services (CFSA) agency. The crack cocaine epidemic was escalating, and children and families were suffering.

Our local Fox Five News station aired a nightly program called City Under Siege that showed the carnage of the drug wars in our city. It covered the drive-by shootings, the drug raids, and the images of young Black boys' dead bodies riddled with bullets on D.C. streets. It was a stressful and horrific time. I made home visits to many unsafe and crime-ridden neighborhoods.

My job was to investigate child neglect and abuse complaints. Every day I went to work to make a difference, but the reality of being injured loomed large in my mind. I worried if I would take a stray bullet from a drive-by or be carjacked while I was in the field. My sensitive personality was overwhelmed by the shear level of stress.

I developed vicarious trauma.

My stress response was in overdrive. Although I was stressed out, I had a job to do. My desire to provide for my children and to help neglected and abused children was stronger than any fear of being injured. I often look back in disbelief and wonder how I made it through it all. I believed my grandparents were with me every day. I remember removing children from a home in a high-crime area in one of the most dangerous parts of the city at the time.

The children were left home alone; the house was filthy. The children were afraid and traumatized and apparently had not eaten in a while. The only food I had in my car was a pack of crackers. I will never forget their reaction when I reached out my hand with the crackers to give them. Without any emotion, they snatched the crackers so fast and swallowed them—it did not look real. They did not stop to chew. It was like a magic trick, but it was not. It was their reaction to being starved.

I was saddened by how they were treated. I couldn't get these images and the pain these children endured out of my mind at the end of day. It bothered me how they were treated by the people who should have protected, nurtured, and love them.

After two-and-a-half years in that position, a co-worker who had joined a newly created department at Child and Family Services Administration, called Families Together, asked me to join him. I was hired to work in a group of specially trained social workers whose job it was to keep families together. The work was known as family preservation.

In my first training, instructors told me that during home visits always to place my back to a solid wall in the house. It was a way to protect myself from a stray bullet entering the home. Constant violence and the threat of death were a daily reality. I provided parenting training, crisis counseling, transportation to community organizations for food and medical care, taught conflict resolution, mentored children, and made referrals to community services agencies. I worked with children who were exposed to toxic stress and complex trauma and who were on constant alert (vigilance). I helped them to co-regulate, played with them like they were my own children, and served as a life coach for their parents and when necessary advocated for them.

In this position, I worked with two families for a month. I was on call 24 hours a day and wore a pager. One case involved an elderly man in his mid-sixties. I was sent out to a house for reports of child neglect. It was in early March after a major storm had fallen on DC. As the ice began to melt outside on a cold but sunny day, I approached his three story, older home in a residential neighborhood. I knocked on the door several times and did not get a response. I had almost walked away then the door slowly opened. An elderly Black man, unshaved, hunchbacked with a cane appeared. His nose was running, eyes drooping, he looked depressed, as if he had the weight of the world on his shoulders. I introduced myself and told him I was sent by my agency to help him. I was with a program called Families Together.

He was not impressed. He said, "Are you here to take my children from me?"

I responded, "No sir, I am here to help you keep them with you."

Doubtful he added, "The only person who can help me is God."

I responded, "Maybe God sent me here as a vessel to help you, give me a chance." He let me enter his home. His three young children were huddled together in another small room. They had colds but seemed well taken care of, for the most part. The children ranged in age from 3 to 8 years old. I told him I would help him find a new place to live if he trusted me. He responded, I only trust in God. If you think you can help me, go right ahead and do it.

I said, "I have a friend who is a reporter with the *Washington Post*. He can write a story about your family and people will help you." He seemed unfazed. But he gave me the okay to make the call. I called the reporter, and he went to the house the next day.

The story about the man with his three young children appeared in the paper. People from everywhere donated thousands of dollars and someone called with a renovated three-bedroom apartment. A young police officer woman volunteered to take the kids to her family's house, and they did the girls hair and became a surrogate family for the children. Her family stepped up to parent those children and provided a loving home. I will never forget the day the elderly man saw his new apartment. I handed him the keys. We walked into the apartment. He looked around in awe, smiled, and cried. Then he said, Thank God.

In 1994, Katherine Boo, an award-winning author and journalist, arrived at the Child and Family Services Administration (CFSA), seeking to write a story about the Families Together program. Fearing an exposé type of story, four social workers in my unit declined. I eagerly accepted the offer. I had been working hard with families and it was my moment to show it. Katherine Boo went out in the field with me for seven months. She witnessed firsthand my efforts to keep children and families together during some tumultuous times. On October 29th, 1995, her cover story in the *Washington Post* titled, "Saving Families, One-on-One: Difficulty of Preserving Homes Takes Its Toll on Social Worker" appeared. It was nominated for a Pulitzer Prize. The job had taken a toll on me emotionally.

CHAPTER 36

From Chronic
Stress to Resilience

In 1995, I left CFSA and went to work for the DC Public Schools System helping students with severe to profound disabilities. It was another stressful but rewarding job. The principal, LaGrande Lewis, was a special person. Her kindness, love, and advocacy for her students and staff never waned during my 13 years there. She loved those students and staff. She went above and beyond to help everybody. She was a buffer for her students, staff, and families.

My first week on the job, a student came flying by me on his crutches. He fell right in front of me. I reached down to help him. He pushed my hand away and stared at me as if to say, I do not need your help. He jumped up quickly, got back on his crutches, and moved swiftly down the hall. I figured it out. He did not want my pity; he wanted my respect. Over the years, I learned about the downside of ableism and the power of relationships.

I watched some amazing teachers find creative ways to teach, engage, and educate students with disabilities. The students and parents taught me what it meant to be resilient. I met many parents over the years who endured chronic stress. Having a child with a disability, especially a severe to profound disability, is stressful and requires a lot of work to care for them. Their chronic health conditions and ongoing surgeries and rising health care cost are a constant reason for them to worry. Researchers conducted studies on parents and other caretakes of people with disabilities and discovered their stress levels were high and in some cases their telomeres which are the caps on the end of our DNA is significantly frayed, worn down by their chronic stress load caring for their loved ones. I empathized with what they go through to care for their children.

My Aunt Janine had a child born with encephalitis. He was blind and could not walk or sit up. She said, "Doctors told me he would not live to see one-year-old. I was severely stressed and felt guilty having a child with a profound disability. I felt like I had done something wrong to my body to cause his disability, or maybe it was a side effect of a medication. I did not know my child had a disability until he was born. I knew something was wrong when they did not bring him to see me for a while. I was so nervous; I knew something was wrong. Hospital staff put me in a wheelchair and rolled me into another room to see him. When I held him for the first time, I cried.

"I loved my son so much. People were so mean. At his wellness checks, in the waiting room, some people stirred at him like he was a monster. It hurt me terribly and I felt ashamed. And when I saw the other mothers with healthy babies it made me feel sad. I wondered why my baby was born profoundly disabled."

She loved her son dearly.

He was only expected to live for 6 months, but he lived until the age of 4. Her untiring nurturing and love enabled him to live more than three years longer.

She said, he knew who I was. He responded excitedly when he heard my voice, he cried so loud and shook his body forcefully. I had much respect and empathy for my aunt.

She later had two healthy children and was an amazing mother. Attuned and loving. The death of a child is traumatic; you never forget it. The stress of her first son's death stayed with her forever.

Like my aunt, I will always admire, respect, and be humbled by the students' parents I worked with at this school. Not out of pity, but from a place of reverence and great admiration. There was one young mother who brought her son to school sometimes by herself. Maybe he missed his bus, I am not sure, but she transported him to school in her car. Her son was a paraplegic. Because her car was small, I assumed she could not get his wheelchair in it. When she arrived at school, she would carry him herself into the building.

Her love for son and determination were remarkable. But I knew it was taxing on her emotionally and physically.

I have fond memories of helping during Special Olympics events. I witness students smile, who competed in the various events. Being a part of those moments, pushing the wheelchairs during various races was inspiring. The students prepared for the events with hard work, and their excitement was something to behold. Each year they looked forward to showing what they had to beat their competition it was exciting to watch and be a part of.

This job taught me many lessons about the impact of stress on the parents of children with profound disabilities. When I went on field trips with my students, some people stared at us as if we were pariahs. That bothered me.

I started a support group for the parents. We came together on the weekends to talk about the stress associated with parenting a child with a disability. I provided stress management strategies, a place of solace, and friendship. The parents bonded. We talked about self-care. Each parent shared their stories and feelings of having a child with a disability, offered strategies to cope more effectively, and to be together as a group with a mutual passion for their children.

During the first session, I was inspired and humbled by the women's strengths and resilience. The stories they shared about the amount of effort and work they put into caring for their children with minimal help from others, being over worked, and feeling isolated, and alone. It touched my heart. We went on several field trips. We had family outings together; I brought my children along to restaurants. We traveled to Baltimore's African American Museum, to McLean, Virginia to Pet Farm, and other places. We went to LaPlata, Md for Seafood. They felt joy having a place to discuss what it was like to have a child with a disability and to have safe and supportive place to feel heard and know there were other parents going through what they were experiencing. They knew they were not alone.

If you have a child with a disability and you are having some these same challenges, I recommend connecting with a support group. Go online. Google the type of issue or support group or advocacy organization you are interested in. There are countless organizations serving a myriad of concerns available today. If you do not see an organization that fits your needs, start your own support group. I believe in self-care and advocating for oneself. For example, one year a staff person was frustrated because we had no venue for the student's graduation.

The gym was a logical place to have it, but it was old and had not been refurbished in a long time. I was moved to help the students have a memorable graduation. I asked my wife and children to help me paint and refinish the entire parquet hardwood floor, along with replacing some missing concrete blocks in the walls. Exposing my kids to community service early in life was important to me, like my grandfather had taught me so many years ago. I remember after the gym was finished, with a fresh coat of paint and newly refinished floor, the students smiling. You could tell right away the difference in their attitude and mood. Being in a bright and welcoming environment lifted their mood. Their smiling faces were the last image I had of those students before I transferred to another school.

CHAPTER 37

My Life has
Come Full Circle

For nearly 30 years, I have been a social worker in the same public school system I attended as a child. It's the same public-school system that my grandfather walked a 5-year-old, scared, crying little boy with separation anxiety through its doors on the first day of kindergarten a long time ago. Now all these years later I stand courageous, confident, vulnerable, and a self-actualized professional public servant.

Truly my life has come full circle. Throughout my life, mental health has been a focus of my personal and professional career. I have become keenly aware of the role stress has played in shaping who I am, both good and bad. Having positive and caring people in my life mattered. Regardless of what you are going through no matter how hard life is for you, unfair, we can bounce back. Adversity and stress are unavoidable. We all face our share of the pain it goes with the territory. It's not what happens to us but how we respond that matters. But you cannot do it alone. Sometimes you need help and that's what I have done throughout my career. Try to make a positive difference in the lives of others and seek support from trusted friends and family when necessary.

My school district has made it a priority to be a trauma-sensitive and informed, equity driven, and culturally sensitive school system. Through the School Behavioral Health Expansion actions mental health initiatives and policies are in place that are making a difference in the lives of countless children and parents in some of the cities marginalized neighborhoods. Every school has mental health clinicians and community partners agencies in the building to address mental health issues impacting children and families. My hope is that we will see more school districts around the country becoming trauma informed. Then more students and parents will get the mental and behavioral health support and services they need.

CHAPTER 38

Adverse Childhood
Study (ACE's)

I learned about the Adverse Childhood Experiences (ACE's) study one day while researching material for a professional development workshop on childhood trauma. I watched Dr. Nadine Burke Harris' popular TedTalk on the ACE's study. I was riveted by her TedTalk, how childhood adversity contributes to poor health outcomes in physical, emotional, mental health, and social relationships. She says that a colleague gave her the study to read, and it blew her away. It helped her connect the dots for how she viewed childhood trauma and altered the way she treated her young patients.

She is an Ivy League-educated pediatrician who has served vulnerable children for decades at her pediatric practice in Bayview Hunters Point neighborhood in San Francisco, California. In 2019, Governor Gavin Newsom appointed her the first-ever Surgeon General of California.

The original Adverse Childhood Experiences (ACE's) Study was conducted in the mid-1990s by Dr. Vincent J. Felitti, MD, chief of the Kaiser Medical Permanente Medical Program in San Diego, and Dr. Robert Anda, MD with the Center for Disease Control. They conducted the study to find out if childhood adversity had lifelong health consequences. They created a survey and gave it to 17,000-plus Kaiser Permanente members. The majority were Caucasian, college-educated, middle-class, employed people. They did not fit the stereotypical profile of a population with childhood adversity or trauma.

Dr. Felitti was interested in doing the study after learning from his overweight female patients who lost weight and had put the weight back within a short time that childhood trauma was related to it. He was puzzled by what led to them putting the weight back on. He discovered many of his clients had experienced childhood adversity. Some were sexually abused as children and the weight gain was their maladaptive coping mechanism. He wondered if there was a correlation between childhood adversity and adult mental and behavioral health issues occurring in the broader society. A colleague suggested he use a larger and more diverse group of people to conduct a valid study. He chose to survey Kaiser Permanente members because they had a large and diverse group. The original study had 10 survey questions.

- Child abuse (emotional, physical, sexual
- Child neglect (emotional, physical)
- Mental Illness
- Substance Abuse
- Mother treated Violently
- Incarcerated Relative
- Divorce[9]

The results revealed that childhood adversity is a common problem regardless of race and income. The more aces you experienced as a child without a person to buffer you, the more likely you'd experience physical health problems such as cancer, cardiovascular disease, auto-immune disease, COPD, and more, as well as anxiety and depression and other mental illnesses and interpersonal problems in

---

[9] http://www.joiningforcesforchildren.org/what-are-aces

relationships in adulthood.

As humans, we share the same nervous system. Stress dysregulation weakens the immune system, disrupts hormonal function, and throws the mind and body out of balance. Without bringing the mind-body system back into balance, we suffer the fate of poor health outcomes in adulthood.

Since the original ACE's study in the mid-1990s, many other organizations have conducted their own versions of the ACE's study, adding other adverse life events and stressors such community violence, poverty, racism, other major life events that caused stress and activate the stress response to the questionnaire.

The findings of the ACE's research show that childhood adversity is a widespread and common issue. By knowing this information, you will be more knowledgeable about your risk factors for mental and behavioral health in adulthood. This information can assist you with customizing a self-care plan that address your needs.

The question is why don't our doctors catch it? Because many are not aware of it. They are treating the symptoms and diseases and illness of the ACE's. The ACE's questionnaire must be used along with the depression questionnaire during annual doctor visits. Gathering this information will add another level of informed care to ensure patients are adequately screened for ACE's related health risk factors.

The ACE's study has helped me make sense of the poor health and early deaths of childhood friends who grew up in homes with 5 or more ACE's. Also, it explains the behavioral and emotional and psychological challenges many of the students I've worked with in my over 30-year career. Please go online and take the Adverse Childhood Experiences (ACE's) questionnaire. You may learn something that could be used to improve your health.

CHAPTER 39

Self-Care:
The Start to Healing

My ability to stay mentally healthy and not have a depression relapse over the past 25 years is attributable to self-care. It was a challenge to maintain when my children were younger, because they were my #1 priority. I had to adapt and understand that self-care was not a selfish act but is a responsible one. Self-care has made me a better person, father, husband, friend, and co-worker. By focusing on self-care, I'm more mentally focused, have more energy, and I'm less stressed. Self-care is a great way to manage stress. The stress management activities I mentioned here will help you improve your health, and work through some of your mental and physical challenges that have gone unaddressed for a long time. I like the demonstration that flight attendants give prior to aircraft taking off that illustrates the importance of taking care of oneself first. For example, the flight attendants hold up the oxygen mask and say and the event the aircraft is in distress, and we lose oxygen fix the mask over your face first. Use the oxygen to stay conscious so you can assist others dependent people, such as a child. If you pass out, you won't be available to help your child or anyone else.

It can be customized to fit your individual needs. I replaced an unhealthy lifestyle by exercising, eating better, thinking more positively, using mindfulness mediation, breathing exercises, and bibliotherapy to improve my health. For people with traumatic experiences, Dr. Bessel

Vander Kolk recommends yoga as a form of self-care and therapy to best address the deep wounds of trauma and somatic symptoms many people have expressed are problematic and are, in some cases, debilitating.

I once weighed 300 pounds. I got down to 230 pounds by going to the YMCA to work out and use the treadmill. I had a daily practice of walking in nature. Living in Washington DC at the time, I went to the National Mall and walked near the monuments and along the Potomac River; it was relaxing. I forced myself to walk every day, and the weight started coming off. My mental health improved.

I bought a bicycle and went riding as much as I could. One of my personality traits as a sensitive person is overthinking and sensory overload. I used Cognitive Behavior Therapy (CBT) to change my thinking and behavior to be less reactive to stress. It is a therapy created in the 1960s by Dr. Aaron Temkin (Tim) Beck; he's an icon in the field of psychiatry. While working with his patients with depression, he noticed that when their thoughts were pessimistic, he believed it contributed to their mental state. It made sense that negative thinkers would view life from that distorted lens. That type of thinking becomes a self-fulfilling philosophy.

He believed that people with depression may have developed their gloomy mindsets in childhood. Whether through how they view themselves or a learned behavior from family members. Cognitive Behavior Therapy (CBT) principles are based on the idea that our thoughts/cognitions (either rational, distorted, or irrational) influence the way we feel and behave. The way we interpret situations and life experiences results in a myriad of problematic or beneficial outcomes. We have different personalities and thinking patterns, those of us who have anxiety disorders and depression are prone to have distorted thinking based on faulty beliefs and assumptions. Some of us overreact and catastrophize thinking the worst-case scenario. Human emotions and thoughts drive our behavior with this approach you can look at problems and stressors differently. I grew up watching and listening to people tell themselves all sorts of irrational, unrealistic things that were destructive. Others who were more upbeat, positive, hopeful, made good decisions and their lives turned out better. CBT fit perfectly with lessons I learned as child. My grandfather always saw the glass half-filled versus half empty, a reference to having a positive perspective on things.

I use bibliotherapy. It's a great form of therapy, at least it was for me. I learned a lot of different cognitive and behavioral strategies to use to improve my mental and physical health. I had to learn how to use my own healing power of my mind to improve my health and emotional wellbeing. I read many books about mindfulness and mediation. My friend Jane Rand had referred to John Kabat's Zinn's book, *The Full Life Catastrophe*; I loved it. I began a daily practice of mindfulness, focusing on the present moment and doing breathe work. I found a quiet place to sit or lay still and focused on breathing from the diaphragm and centering the mind by being conscious of the breath. There are many ways to practice mindful breathing. Nowadays, I use YouTube and other popular social media sites; they are a valuable source of information on all things, particularly stress management strategies.

One great thing about mindfulness is that it's easy to do, and it can be done anywhere. Preferably in a quiet place with no distractions. When I did have panic attacks, I would lie down on my back and slowly breathed in to count of 1-2-3-4 and exhaled to count of 1-2-3-4. When my mind raced with crazy thoughts like I was dying, I used self-talk. I said to myself, no you are fine. Relax and focus on your breathing. Over time this practice tamed my monkey mind to be still and obey me. Soon my panic attacks subsided. Another good book is Herbert Benson, *The Relaxation Response*. I recommend it for learning how to relax the mind-body and activate the parasympathetic nervous systems known as the rest and digest system.

In Conclusion, writing this book has been a journey. Through many starts and stops, struggles, self-doubt, and adversary. I'm proud I never gave up. I hope it will inspire many people, motivate others, and help many not feel ashamed of their mental illness. I'm wiser and braver for having stuck with it through adversary as is the case with life. My life's journey proves not to judge people by their race, sexuality, religion, socioeconomic status, their looks, or mental health challenges. In fact, don't judge people at all. Be patient, be kind, and when people falter doesn't be so quick to give up on. Beneath the surface are many unknown forces swaying our thinking and behavior. As they say, don't ask what's wrong with him/her, ask what happened? Then show compassion, empathy, and be supportive in any way that you can.